UPHOLDING THE VISION

SERVING THE POOR IN TRAINING AND BEYOND

THIRD EDITION

Christian Community Health Fellowship

Memphis, TN

Acknowledgements

We are grateful to the authors of each of the chapters in this book for their willingness to allow us to use their material. But even more than that, we are grateful for their examples of what it means to live out the gospel through healthcare and other ministries among the underserved.

Executive Editor: Steve Noblett
Editor Emeritus: David Caes
Copy Editor: Cinelle Barnes
Layout: Sarah Dickert
Cover Design: Jason Stevens
Proofreaders: Kristy Tarrant
                   Andrew Kim

ISBN 978-0-692-59328-8

Publisher
Christian Community Health Fellowship
2595 Central Avenue
Memphis, TN 38104

TABLE OF CONTENTS

(continued)

FOREWORD

John Perkins

In the late 1970's and early 1980's we became aware of a crisis among the poor in America in the area of healthcare. Most communities of need were virtually without healthcare, and it was affecting everything – children's performance in school, generational poverty, the ability for people who wanted to work to be able to do so. The crisis had been there for a long time, but we suddenly became alert to it, and felt it was time for us to do something to serve those most in need. Some of us started small health centers to address the crisis. Back then there were only a few young people who felt called to this mission, and not many of them were providers. However, we moved ahead because of the great need. With the help of a small group of friends, I helped start a clinic in my hometown of Mendenhall, Mississippi. It was extremely difficult to find doctors for small Southern towns. We came to see this as our biggest challenge. We needed a way to connect with Christian providers who were willing to serve the poor. This was the motivation for the birth of CCHF.

As I look around the country, I see many Christian clinics and health centers bringing healing to the lives of the people who are so broken. Both the providers and their patients are experiencing Christian growth and development. But far more is happening. Those working in these centers are joining hands with their patients and becoming servants in their communities, addressing issues of need and justice, and working together to build up these broken neighborhoods. They are doing the hard work of breaking down racial and cultural barriers, and becoming the bridges of peace by living out the true Gospel of Jesus Christ.

Healthcare professionals have the unique ability to attract resources that our people need, and to see healing take place at a broader level. As healers we must learn to think past just providing care for the physical body. We must be concerned about spiritual care, mental health care, and the restoration of families. We are able to encourage better education and better methods of education in these places, and to empower people who have been pushed to the bottom of society to find the abundant life that Jesus promises us.

This kind of thinking requires real courage. I am excited about the growing number of young people today who see overcrowded schools, under-resourced communities, places of anger and violence and lack of leadership and of low quality of life, and who don't avoid those places, but run into those places to serve them and love them with the love of Christ. It requires faith and a willingness to make sacrifices – a willingness to share in the pain of the people they serve, and to walk with the people and make those challenges their shared challenges. God is raising up intelligent and courageous doctors, dentists, nurses, psychologists and other health workers who are using their skills to bring wholistic healing where brokenness is rampant. These make up a new generation of faith followers of Jesus, who do not simply see brokenness and need, but who also see Christ in the midst of it all. These are prisoners of hope who believe that Christ can heal and restore individuals and the communities where they live.

Jesus said, "I have come that you might have life and that you have it more abundantly." What Christ wants in healthcare today is for providers to care about the whole individual and the whole community. This new concept is what the CCHF movement is all about.

Here is your opportunity to do more than just make a living practicing medicine. It is practicing medicine as you live for Christ. Jesus gives us the opportunity to bring hope and joy to places where resources are the most scarce. This is a profound way to live. This, in fact, is the Body of Christ, the true and authentic church. It is the outliving of the in-living of Christ.

John Perkins was instrumental in founding Christian Community Health Fellowship in 1978. The founders worked to craft CCHF as a place for disciples to connect to discuss and learn what it means to provide distinctively Christian healthcare – to address the question, "Is there a difference between being a Christian in medicine, and practicing Christian medicine?"
Dr. Perkins continues to be a vital part of CCHF and speaks at each of our annual conferences. Dr. Perkins has been a living brochure for the mission and values of CCHF, living out the principles of compassion, justice, creativity, and personal sacrifice in a way that generations can follow.
Read more about John Perkins at www.jvmpf.org.

INTRODUCTION

Steve Noblett

"We envision a movement of God's people who choose daily to minister healing to marginalized communities in the name of Jesus."

We envision a movement because it will take a movement.

The need across our nation is staggering. Twenty-five percent of Americans live in areas designated as "medically-underserved." These areas have the greatest needs, and yet the least medical resources. Patients in these communities have to compete with one another for doctors. And those who win are not those with the greatest needs, but rather, those with the greatest means. Over ninety million Americans live in medically-underserved and health professional shortage areas; and for that, we need a movement.

The movement we envision is a movement of God's people. The problem is not one of resource, but of brokenness. America has the best medical training institutions in the world. She has the greatest medical technology and the finest hospitals. As a citizenry we spend more per person on healthcare than any country – almost double what every other developed nation spends. And yet more people in our country struggle with barriers that prohibit them from accessing healthcare. When compared to every other first-world nation, Americans rank near the bottom on almost every major health indicator. We are sicker and die sooner than people in other developed nations, and often cannot get the help we need. The system is broken. It needs serious repair, and that must begin by addressing the moral foundations upon which it operates.

Isaiah 58 promises that if we honor the Lord by seeking justice for the poor, that he will make us "restorers" and "repairers."[1] Jesus also taught us to pray: Thy kingdom come, thy will be done on earth as it is in heaven.[2] In that short little phrase, he reveals that God seeks consistency between the standards of heaven and the realities of earth. Justice, righteousness, and wholeness – shalom – are the very things he instructs us to long for and work toward. God does not have a double standard. If it is not good enough for heaven, then we are not to be satisfied with it on earth.

Only a few verses later Christ instructs us to "seek first the kingdom of God and his righteousness, and all these things shall be added unto you."[3] God intends to work here on earth by working through his people – you and me – to reconcile broken people and the broken systems they've created to himself and to his kingdom. These may seem like colossal tasks, but Christ's death was sufficient for both our sins and their consequences. This hope we have is certain.

It is this hope that allows us to envision a movement of God's people who will faithfully represent, demonstrate, and proclaim the gospel of the kingdom among those who are poor and marginalized, and to the broken institutions that make up our society.

We have this vision because we see it in the life and ministry of Jesus Christ, and because he has called and empowered us to serve in the same way. Over the years, this vision has become clearer to us, and we have seen it grow. It is now so much a part of our own souls that it impacts everything we do, almost without our thinking about it.

A vision for justice in healthcare, for the health and welfare of all people, and for the power of Christ to be demonstrated through compassion and healing has always been an essential part of the good news of the kingdom. Jesus made healing a significant part of his ministry. The inaugural sermon that would define his work talked about proclaiming good news to the poor, freedom to prisoners and the oppressed, and recovery of sight for the blind.[4]

When Jesus sent out the twelve, and later, the seventy-two, he gave them authority to heal every disease and sickness, and he commanded them to proclaim the kingdom gospel and heal the sick.[5] In Acts 10, when Peter proclaimed the gospel to the seekers at Cornelius' house, he described Jesus as being anointed by the Holy Spirit to do good and to heal all who were under the power of the devil.[6] Physical healing of the sick and infirm was a central part of the ministry of Jesus.

Before his crucifixion, Jesus proclaimed that those who would follow him in faith would continue the works he had been doing, and his earliest disciples upheld this very vision.[7] The apostles continued the healing ministry of Christ. Those who we traditionally understand as the first deacons performed signs and wonders, specifically healing the sick.[8] Paul and Barnabas continued the healing ministry of Jesus, as did ordinary disciples such as Ananias of Damascus.[9]

In his final parable of the rewarding of the "sheep" and the judgment of the "goats" at the end of the age, Jesus said that we would be judged in part based on whether we did or did not visit the sick and show compassion for them.[10] In the church, he has provided gifts of healing.[11] We are instructed to call for our church elders when we are sick so that we might confess our sins and be healed by the prayer of faith.[12] God wants us to experience healing and to share healing with others. In fact, based on Scripture, God rarely heals apart from doing it through his people. Because community is his nature, God chooses to reach the sick and needy in this collective, relational way.

The early church understood this. While there are examples of special places for the care of certain classes of the sick, it was in the third century that the first "hospitals" were created by Christian fathers to care for all who were suffering, including the poor and outcast. Basil the Great stands as a fascinating early church figure, who built a hospice for the sick where the poor and privileged alike would receive equal medical care, where physicians would be housed, and where research could take place. The people of the time nicknamed it "The New City" because they deemed it to resemble what the kingdom of God must look like.[13] Other early church figures like St.

Sampson the Hospitable, were notable in the formation of the hospital movement, which received its name from the Christian practice of hospitality.

Healthcare continued as an essential function of the church through the Middle Ages and into the Renaissance. Later on in America, prior to the Civil War, sick care outside of the home tended to be delivered by a pastor or church leader. Though little resemblance remains between medical instruction then and what it is now, training in the healing arts occurred as an essential part of pastoral ministry in the 1700s and early 1800s. John Wesley wrote numerous medical journals. While no one considers Wesley a medical expert, it demonstrates that both physical and spiritual care were integral to ministry.

It was in the mid-nineteenth century when prevailing worldviews dichotomized the spiritual from the physical. Evangelical Christianity began to shift its focus away from caring for our bodies to focusing on evangelism and spirituality. The gospel of the kingdom was replaced over time by a gospel of salvation, and saving souls became the primary goal. Eventually the kingdom was spiritualized as an ideal, or as a place we will go when we die. The believers of the day, whether knowingly or unknowingly, made the kingdom seem intangible, and no longer "at hand" or "among you."

Nevertheless, even with the disintegration of the physical and spiritual, there were those who continued to uphold the vision. Churches continued to engage in care for the sick, though in a different function. Many, if not the majority, of medical schools in America that sprang up in the late 1700s through the mid-1800s, were founded and governed by church denominations. When post-war industrialization brought about major public health challenges due to urbanization, Protestant and Catholic groups founded hospitals in response to these needs. Though today few remain connected to their original faith mission, most of the hospitals in our cities bear names that echo their Christian roots.

It is a sad reality that for one hundred and fifty years the church's historical connection to hospitality and care for the sick waned in America. But there were still those who upheld the vision. In the last two decades we have seen a rebound across the nation. The church is recovering the gospel of the kingdom. Justice and compassion for the poor and the sick are once again becoming essential ministries of the church. The landscape of healthcare is changing rapidly, and we need to help Jesus' bride understand how to responsibly engage in ministries of healing and justice. The flame has not gone out. It is burning, growing, rising, and getting brighter.

The movement we envision took a great leap forward in the 1970s when a disconnected group of young medical disciples began asking, "Is there a difference between being a Christian doctor, and practicing Christian medicine?"

"If Jesus were a physician in the twentieth century, how would he practice?"

There had always been Christians in medicine, and many of them saw their medical careers as a calling to serve Christ by serving others. But now the question became, "If God had chosen to send Jesus as a physician in the twentieth century, how would he practice differently than we have been trained to practice?"

In several places, Christian medical pioneers started clinics to explore what "Christian healthcare" might look like. Dr. Peter Boelens and a team of medical missionaries from the Luke Society started a work in the Mississippi Delta, and wrote about their experiences. Dr. Janelle Goetcheus and her husband, Allen, moved from a small town in Indiana to Washington, DC, to care for their homeless neighbors. Her work attracted attention, largely because Dr. Goetcheus relentlessly challenged the practice of local hospitals that treated insured patients differently than those who were poor but just as sick.

Dr. Bill Morehouse opened a clinic in Rochester, NY, the birthplace of family medicine as a specialty. He and his wife, Susan, quickly began to see that the needs in the clinic were related to broader needs in the community, and they began integrating community outreach and community development into an integral part of their health ministry.

A group of medical missionaries working in Appalachia began thinking in terms of justice for the poor, and began incorporating spiritual care into physical care – as they had seen on the foreign mission field. The work there looked like something you might see in a third-world country, but it was done with excellence and with much grace, compassion, and a commitment to reflect Biblical principles and values.

Other Christian health professionals began to ask the same questions. They started health ministries with a vision to more faithfully stand for God's values as reflected in the kingdom of God. Ministries began in places like Austin, IL; New Hebron, MS; Denver; Richmond; Chicago; Pittsburg; Philadelphia; and Memphis. This second wave of pioneers built on what they had seen in Washington, the Mississippi Delta, and Appalachia.

It was this group that started Christian Community Health Fellowship (CCHF). CCHF began in 1978 with a dual mission of being a community of Christians who would encourage and support one another as they lived out the gospel through healthcare among the poor; and to be a prophetic voice, calling the church back to its Biblical role to care for the sick, the poor and the stranger.

There have been many milestones over the past thirty-seven years of CCHF. At the publication of this edition, there are roughly three hundred clinics that are open full-time, and that seek to deliver distinctively Christian primary healthcare in marginalized communities across the country. In addition to those who are working in those clinics, there are several thousand Christian providers and executive leaders who are walking out their calling to preach and heal among the poor in secular settings – hospitals, non-faith-based clinics, residency programs, and universities.

This book is a collection of their stories, their thoughts and experiences, and their motivations for upholding the vision. We are still a community of seekers, constantly asking questions and challenging ourselves to be more faithful to Christ and his kingdom as we extend his love to our marginalized neighbors.

As you read the following chapters, I hope that you will come away with the following convictions that will shape your future as a health professional and Christ-follower:

1. **Your medical training is more than a career choice. It is a calling to serve Christ missionally.** Because this is a calling, Christ is committed to shape not only your skills and abilities, but your life and character. If you allow him to challenge and refine the things that motivate you, he will do great things through you.

2. **Mission is not something you plan to do one day, or something that happens for a couple of weeks in the summer.** Mission is a lifestyle. Serving Christ intentionally as a daily choice is the most fulfilling way to live your life. To serve Christ missionally will always involve serving those who are poor, orphaned, widowed, and estranged.

3. **Humility is the distinct trait of those who live out the gospel through healthcare.** Commit to being a life-long seeker who desperately wants to live and practice in such a way that reflects Christ's character and mission. Humility allows you to be a learner who asks God to lead you instead of asking him to bless you as you go your own chosen way.

4. **Expect suffering and hardship.** It is the path that Jesus walked, and he calls us to follow him. Jesus will lead you into harm's way, but he will always go with you. If you follow, you will suffer. But you will have no regrets.

5. **You are not alone.** There is a nationwide community of disciples who are committed to the same vision, and who are willing to encourage you, counsel you, pray for you, and partner with you. A big part of your success will depend on your finding them and becoming relationally engaged with them.

I pray that Christ's vision for the church and for the indomitable advance of his kingdom grips your life and ruins you for everything else, as it has done for me and those who have contributed to this book. It excites me to dream about how you and others in your generation will see beyond what we have seen, and will build beyond what we have built. Our testimony is that the vision is real, God is faithful, and that the sacrifice is worth it.

THE NEED

CHAPTER

HE'S MY DADDY

Anonymous

To each staff member of this facility:

As you pick up that chart today and scan that green Medicaid card, I hope you will remember what I am about to say.

I spent yesterday with you. I was there with my mother and father. We didn't know where we were supposed to go or what we were supposed to do, for we had never needed your services before. We have never before been labeled "charity."

Yesterday, I watched as my daddy became a diagnosis, a chart, a case number, a charity case labeled "no sponsor" because he had no health insurance.

I saw a weak man in line, waiting for five hours to be shuffled through a system of impatient office workers, burned-out nursing workers, and a budget-scarce facility, being robbed of any dignity and pride he may have left. I was amazed at how impersonal your staff was, huffing and blowing when the patient did not present the correct form, speaking carelessly of other patients' cases in front of passersby, of lunch breaks that would be spent away from this poor man's hell.

My dad is only a card, a file number to clutter your desk on appointment day, a patient who will ask for directions twice after they've been given the first time. But, no, that's not really my dad. That's only what you see.

What you don't see is a cabinetmaker since the age of fourteen, a self-employed man who has a wonderful wife, four grown kids (who visit too much), and five grandchildren (with two more on the way) – all of whom think their "pop" is the greatest. This man is everything a daddy should be – strong and firm, yet tender; rough around the edges; a country boy, yet respected by prominent business leaders.

He's my daddy, the man who raised me

Never lose sight of the people behind your charts. Each chart represents a person with feelings, a history, a life whom you have the power to touch for one day by your words and actions.

through thick and thin, gave me away as a bride, held my children at their births, stuffed a twenty-dollar bill in my hand when times were tough, and comforted me when I cried. Now we are told that before long cancer will take this man away from us.

You may say these are the words of a grieving daughter lashing out in helplessness at the prospect of losing a loved one. I would not disagree. Yet I urge you not to discount what I say. Never lose sight of the people behind your charts. Each chart represents a person – with feelings, a history, a life – whom you have the power to touch for one day by your words and actions. Tomorrow it may be your loved one – your relative or neighbor – who turns into a case marker, a card, a name to be checked off with a yellow marker as done for the day.

I pray that you reward the next person you greet at your station with a kind word or smile, because that person is someone's daddy, husband, wife, mother, son, or daughter – or simply because he or she is a human being, created and loved by God, just as you are.

This letter was dropped off in the outpatient clinic of a large teaching hospital.

CHAPTER 2

WITNESS TO INJUSTICE

Myron Glick

As a young family physician who had just finished medical school and residency, I was faced with a compelling question that was not at all easy to grapple with. What did it mean for me to follow Jesus as a doctor? How would Jesus respond if he were a physician in our world today?

My initial answer to these questions was to forgo the high-paying job, prestige, and reputation, and instead move to Buffalo's West Side with my wife, take out a bank loan, and start a medical practice in a space provided by our church. I, along with other members of the community, started Jericho Road Community Health Center in 1997 as a response to Jesus' call: act justly, love mercy, and walk humbly.[1] We wanted to provide excellent medical care to the poor and vulnerable in order to demonstrate the love of Jesus in a real and tangible way. Though this decision cost us everything, and although the way has not been easy, it remains as a decision we don't regret – not even for a minute. God has been unfathomably faithful to our marriage, our family, and our ministry at Jericho Road, where we provide a culturally-sensitive medical home for refugee and low-income community members.

Our first year of operation, I wondered what it was that Jesus had called me to witness. My answer came in the form of a sixty-two-year old man who was a laborer and was uninsured. He came in to see me so I could fix his hernia. What I saw shocked me. He had an inguinal hernia larger than his hand, and had not received medical care for it prior to that visit. He had been unable to afford the necessary repairs, and did not want to leave his family in medical debt. I tried to find a surgeon to fix the hernia, but nobody agreed to fix it. Several years later, the same patient came in with a new onset of hoarseness. That time, I discovered a large tumor in his throat from which he died a few years later. His suffering and death became a real-life reminder to me early in my career that our healthcare system operated unjustly and with much brokenness. And it was to that injustice Jesus had called me not merely to witness, but to help fight.

I am convinced more than ever that God is on the side of the poorest and most vulnerable in our society.

That mission remains as true and as clear today. Our medical and program staff at Jericho Road – two hundred servant-hearted folks – is diverse, sacrificial, and focused on our mission to demonstrate the love of Jesus to the people we interact with daily. Jericho Road would not exist today except for the decision of these people to take seriously the radical call to be witnesses for, and of service to, "the least of these."

Now almost eighteen years later, I am convinced more than ever that God is on the side of the poorest and most vulnerable in our society. As a physician, I fully believe that those of us who take seriously the call to follow Jesus must use our gifts, talents, personalities, histories, relationships, and influence to walk alongside those who have need. I do not think we can opt out of this basic Biblical mandate. It is not an option.

A Witness for the Least of These

In Matthew 25, Jesus reminds his followers that they had fed him when he was hungry, clothed him when he was naked, and visited him when he was in prison. His followers protested by saying they had never seen Jesus hungry or naked or in prison. But then Jesus said something incredibly profound that should motivate each of us: As you did it to the least of these, you did it as unto me.

Isaiah 58 is another example of God's heart for justice for the poor. In this chapter, God makes it clear that he is not impressed by expressions of religiosity that have no influence on the way one actually lives, but rather, he is deeply moved when we humble ourselves, share our bread with the poor, provide shelter to the homeless, clothe the naked, and fight against oppression. His call to justice is this: Love your neighbor as yourself and do unto others as you would want them to do to you.

I am often reminded by the difficult situations we encounter at Jericho Road to treat every patient the way I would want my own mother or child to be treated. When I remember this simple truth, it motivates me to care, to advocate, and to do all I can for my patients, especially those who are gravely ill and uninsured.

People who do not have health insurance mostly opt out of seeking medical care unless they experience an emergency. The uninsured tend to forgo routine health screening, examinations, mammograms, and colonoscopies. Chronic ailments such as diabetes, hypertension, and heart disease are often missed. Uninsured adults in America are at least twenty-five percent more likely to die prematurely than adults with coverage. In 2010, twenty-six thousand Americans died prematurely (between ages 25 and 64) as a direct result of lack of health insurance coverage.[2]

In reading Scripture, I get a glimpse of an aching passion for the kingdom of God to be real not only in eternity, but right here and right now.

But then even when people do have health insurance, it does not mean that they will be treated in a just manner within the healthcare system. Seventy-six percent of our patients at Jericho Road have Medicaid as their insurance provider. While this gives them access to basic primary care, we sometimes struggle to get them specialty care when needed. I remember a cardiologist telling me over the phone that he did not see Medicaid patients, and that he recommended these patients to schedule with the hospital residency clinic so that, in his words, "the residents could get some practice."

In Buffalo, there are no private practice psychiatrists who accept Medicaid patients. So where a patient with mental illness goes and whom he or she sees depends strictly on the type of health insurance he or she has. Dermatologists, rheumatologists, and plastic surgeons are hard to find for the patients who come to Jericho Road. And nationally, the same injustice is found.

In Chicago, researchers posed as mothers of sick children who needed specialty care. The researchers called specialty clinics to schedule appointments for their children. When they identified their insurance coverage as private, they were only denied a timely appointment eleven percent of the time. But when they identified their insurance coverage as Medicaid, they were denied a timely appointment sixty-six percent of the time. Medical discrimination exists against the "least of these."[3]

A Witness for the Homeless and Estranged

At Jericho Road, we provide medical care to over a thousand patients per week, and sixty percent of those patients do not speak English. Many of them are refugees – peoples of many nations, estranged from their homelands due to persecution or poverty, and unqualified for insurance. They fit the description of the outsider that Jesus often talks about: without a home, without food, and with very little financial or societal value. While our presence in Buffalo has not completely redeemed the healthcare system, it is true that today, the refugees and the most vulnerable in our area have been better cared for than before, and that others have begun to notice our work, and in some ways, have begun to emulate us.

An injustice that we often witness is when our refugee patients receive care in the hospital or specialty doctor's office without the dignity of having language-appropriate translation. Even though it is the law for doctors to provide interpreters, we see that this is not often done. Children are asked to interpret for their parents as they deal with chronic illnesses. Husbands interpret for their spouses, who often present symptoms of abuse. When a non-English-speaking woman is in labor, doctors and nurses use the hospital's language phone-line to try to communicate with her as she moans in pain during a contraction, or as she prepares to deliver the baby. It is costly for doctors and hospitals to underwrite translation services, and sometimes the fee for translation services is more than what the insurance company would agree to reimburse for the entire visit. We have found solutions to this injustice: to advocate for Medicaid and other insurance companies to reimburse the cost of translation; to encourage hospitals and practices to hire staff that reflect the diversity of the communities they serve; and for hospital and physician systems to do the just and right thing, even when it is costly. America is becoming increasingly diverse, and so the care we provide to the refugee and the immigrant should reflect the quality of care we would expect for our family members and ourselves.

A Witness to Many Nations
In 2014, when the new wave of Ebola hit, I became a witness to the even more shocking injustice entrenched in other parts of the world. Jericho Road runs a primary health center in the poorest district of Sierra Leone, one of the most impoverished countries in the world. Because of poverty, recent civil war, ineffective government, colonialism, exploitation by foreign mining companies, and now, Ebola, this amazing country depends on a horribly broken healthcare system with a functionality that is close to none.

In the Kono District, where our clinic is located, two of every five children die by the age of five. Women die during childbirth. The average life expectancy is only forty-five years old. In this district, over four hundred and fifty thousand people rely on three doctors and one hospital that provide only the most basic services. This hospital has no ultrasound machine, no x-ray machine, and no CT scanner. The three doctors and handful of nurses work with one microscope. The basic surgeries performed are C-sections, hernia repairs, and exploratory laparotomies for acute abdominal pain. People become blind in this district at an early age because they have no access to eyeglasses or cataract surgery. Children die of preventable diseases such as malaria, typhoid, pneumonia, and diarrhea. Malnutrition lowers the immune system function of many, making them more susceptible to deathly tuberculosis and AIDS.

In Sierra Leone, Ebola has a mortality rate of up to seventy percent because it is challenging to provide even basic medical care such as IV fluids. Ebola experts believe that the mortality rate of this disease could be decreased to ten percent if they had access to medical care that we take for granted in this country – such as rehydration with IV fluids, monitoring of fluids and electrolytes, and provision of renal dialysis and other organ-support systems. That an infectious disease like Ebola kills the poor in Sierra Leone in such high numbers is an incredibly discouraging truth. It stands as a strong example of injustice in our world. I believe that this is not what God intends. It must break his heart.

A Witness to the Cost of Healthcare

The cost of necessary medications can also be a major challenge for the uninsured, under-insured, or even folks with insurance. Many elderly patients on a fixed social security income struggle to afford the lists of medications their doctors prescribe. It is not unusual for us to see a patient who was seen in the ER, diagnosed with an infection, and prescribed a medication they cannot afford – and so they go without the drugs and get sicker.

I've witnessed several circumstances in which the cost of healthcare has prohibited someone from getting well. I had one patient with private health insurance who was unable to afford the co-pay for her insulin because it was over seven hundred dollars a month. I've read about the new medication being touted to cure Hepatitis C, and how it costs one thousand dollars per pill, and needs to be taken daily for up to three months. Some cancer medications are now costing over one hundred thousand dollars for an entire treatment. Some asthma medications that are used to prevent flare-ups can cost over three hundred dollars per month. Even Viagra, which costs cents to make, is being sold for over twenty dollars per pill – making it difficult for the poor to afford.

Do we want to live in a world where only the rich can afford their well-being? Do we want a nation where children live with chronic asthma because their parents cannot afford their medications, where the elderly scrape by each month in order to sustain their health, and where the treatment of deadly diseases, such as Hepatitis C and cancer, depends on one's having the right kind of health insurance coverage? We daily witness an injustice in such a system, and we cannot help but ask: What would Jesus do?

A Witness Standing in Truth: Righteousness and Justice
In Scripture, the word for righteousness is often interchangeable with the root-word for justice. Too often, we modern-day Christians in America think of righteousness as a call to personal integrity, upright living, and holiness. And this is a call. But it is also so much more.

Righteousness is a call for justice. It is a call to community-wide transformation, and to humble, generous living that impacts both person and society as a whole. It is not only a personal call, but a challenge to the spheres of influence we are a part of, and for citizens of God's kingdom to seek equal and just treatment of all – especially the poor. To be righteous is to live justly. Micah, the prophet, reminds us that God requires us to do justice, love kindness, and live humbly. Followers of Jesus who are in the medical field must not only act with personal integrity, but must also challenge the systems that rule as they operate in unjust manners. It is not okay for a Christian physician to work in a private medical practice that refuses to accept Medicaid patients, or to benefit from a sliding fee scale for the uninsured, or to refuse to provide interpreters for the refugee. We must seek personal righteousness and community justice if we truly are to be followers of Christ.

As a follower of Jesus who has had a front-row seat to how broken and unjust the healthcare system is in this country and in places like the Kono District of Sierra Leone, I must admit that sometimes it is deeply discouraging to witness the suffering on a daily basis, and sometimes I wonder if things will ever change. True system transformation comes slowly and sometimes seems difficult to imagine. So many interests benefit from an unjust structure – the Affordable Care Act notwithstanding. Here again I take solace and inspiration from the Bible.

In reading Scripture, I get a glimpse of an aching passion for the kingdom of God to be real not only in eternity, but right here and right now. In the book of Amos, the prophet calls for the day when "justice will roll down like water and righteousness like a mighty stream." In Revelation 21, there is a proclamation that "he will wipe away every tear from their eyes, and death will be no more, neither shall there be mourning, nor crying, nor pain anymore." I read these verses and feel a longing for righteousness, justice, and the reclamation of God's original intent for his creation. I am encouraged to do what I can as a follower of Jesus to make the kingdom of God real and present this day, this hour, and this moment.

What would happen if every follower of Jesus – especially those of us in medicine – would take seriously his words that continue to echo through history? He says: Care for the least of these, love your neighbors as you love yourselves, and act justly. How would this change our lives, our communities, our clinics, our medical or nursing schools, and our local hospitals? How would this radical call help bring justice and righteousness and transformation to the healthcare system here and abroad?

How? We must seek the answers in prayer and listen closely to the voice of the Rock of Ages.

Myron Glick, MD, is the founder and chief medical officer of Jericho Road Community Health Center. He received a Bachelor of Science degree from Houghton College, is a board-certified family physician, and graduate of the SUNY-Buffalo School of Medicine. He completed his residency training at Lancaster General Hospital in the Family Practice Residency Program and was awarded a fellowship at SUNY-Buffalo Department of Family Medicine in Faculty Development and Primary Care Research. Glick also holds a faculty appointment at SUNY-Buffalo in the School of Medicine.

Glick is a tireless advocate for the poorest and most vulnerable in Buffalo and in places like Sierra Leone. He remains committed to advocating for the day when all people will have access to quality health care simply because all people are created in God's image and so each person has equal worth and should be treated with the utmost dignity and respect.

CHAPTER 3

THE PUBLIC HELL UNDER THE EL

Johanna Berrigan

On our way to the clinic one day, Mary Beth turned to me and said, "I think hell must be a lot like under the El."

This "hell" is the several blocks stretching underneath the elevated train that cuts through Kensington, a neighborhood north of downtown Philadelphia. We drive through it regularly on our way to the St. Francis Inn, the home of the Catholic Worker Free Clinic.

There under the El we encounter a world that is, to say the least, disorienting. The ear-piercing thunder of the train above and raucous din of the traffic of the streets is constant. Lights of all colors glare and flash from storefront windows. Vendors hawk their goods while rap music blasts from every corner as though to drown out the madness. Just before we reach the clinic, we pass the corner bar and rows of abandoned buildings and run-down houses. I can offer only silence in return.

I see desperation and loneliness in the eyes of the men and women. Some, obviously disabled, can barely shuffle down the sidewalk. Some are drunk, others clearly mentally ill. Others lurk between parked cars, trying to sell drugs or themselves.

This is home to the people who come to our clinic, bringing with them the awful effects of poverty, homelessness, mental illness, alcoholism, drug abuse, sexual abuse, and AIDS. Since June 1991, we at the Catholic Worker Free Clinic have been getting to know the inhabitants of this blighted neighborhood. We provide medical care for acute and chronic illnesses and injuries. We do health education. We make referrals for people who do not know where to go. We make home visits for follow-up care regardless of where that takes us – shelters, abandoned buildings, doorways, or the streets. Our call, we believe, is to continue seeing them, extending the mission of the Catholic Worker movement to the area of healthcare.

Community connects me with others who share a call and who can therefore do together what none of us could do separately.

For twelve years before joining the Catholic Worker movement, I worked as a nurse in mainstream hospitals – Catholic hospitals, in fact. Through the years, I had heard about the Catholic Worker movement from friends. I learned that Catholic Worker houses were houses of hospitality, offering a place to live and a family-like environment to people who would otherwise be homeless. I became interested enough to volunteer at the soup kitchen and the clinic run by the Catholic Worker House in Los Angeles. This eventually led to an eight-week summer internship during which I continued to live at home and work at the hospital while driving in whenever possible to participate in the program.

The first night, I saw a nurse practitioner opening her own wallet to give a patient money. The next day, she asked me to drive the woman to an emergency room and promise to visit her the next day. I was struck by how personal the caring was, by the lack of professional distance between the caregiver and the patient. The intake process also impressed me. Patients were asked, "What is your name?" and "What can we do for you?"

Their addresses were written down for follow-up. There were no questions about insurance or income, no forms to fill out to prove eligibility. The kind of care I witnessed that summer so appealed to me that I resigned from my hospital job and joined the Catholic Worker House.

The four years spent living in intentional Christian community, with all its gifts and curses, empowered me to minister in ways previously impossible. When I lived alone, I would often feel sorry for people I saw on the street, but I didn't know how to respond except to send money to some organization. Community connects me with others who share a call and who can therefore do together what none of us could do separately. Community provides the support so essential to carrying the heavy emotional load that goes with immersing ourselves day in and day out in the acute suffering of others. And living in a community committed to simple living minimizes our need for finances so we can devote most of our energy to our vocation, while only using minimal energy on earning money to pay the bills.

Working first in mainstream hospitals and then at Catholic Worker clinics has made me painfully aware of the inequities in this country's healthcare system. The affluent who have adequate medical insurance can, with relative ease, get treatment regardless of their medical problem, mental illness, or addiction. This is not true for the poor. During my encounters with people at the clinic, I am often reminded how radically different their situation would be, what tremendous resources would be available to them, were it not for a healthcare system that largely alienates and excludes the poor. Listening to their stories, I feel anguished, tempered only by a compassion and determination to remain with them, if only to ease their burden for a moment.

Paul tells us that the work of the Holy Spirit in the world is to break down the divisions which separate one group of humans from another. We at the Catholic Worker seek to abandon ourselves to that work of the Holy Spirit. We believe that division between who should and should not receive adequate healthcare should not exist as they do in this country. I know nothing more heartbreaking than to see, as I have seen, our sisters and brothers literally dying on the streets. There is nothing more disconcerting than to see the enormous disparity between what is available and what is provided.

Recently a young woman came into the clinic with numerous complaints: weakness, lack of appetite, stomach pains, inability to sleep, and weight loss. During our conversation, she was in constant motion, playing with the gum in her mouth, rocking from side to side on the bed, and kicking her legs back and forth like a child. As she spoke, she began to cry, staring out the window, tears streaming down her face. It seemed as if she was facing her own pain for the first time. She could no longer take life on the streets, she told us. She was sick, addicted, and emotionally disturbed. She spoke about her life: abandoned by her mother at eight, raped at twelve, pregnant at fourteen. Now, at twenty-eight, she found herself wanting to die rather than go on living this way.

Those who come to the clinic offer us a tremendous grace, revealing to me the beauty of all persons and the great mystery of the love of Christ.

After hours of intensive effort, we finally managed to have her admitted to a nearby psychiatric emergency room. Within an hour, though, personnel from the hospital called us back to say they were going to discharge her. We goaded them into at least keeping her for the night. The next morning she was discharged back onto the streets with no money. They said there was nothing they could do for her, giving her only instructions about admittance into a drug rehabilitation program – for which she would have to wait six weeks.

There she was: physically sick, mentally disturbed, addicted, suicidal – and poor. And because of her poverty, she had no place to go.

At our clinic, we have taken care of persons discharged to the street following major surgery. We have treated persons with serious burns or infected wounds that require a clean dressing change, but the streets are hardly a suitable environment for changing a dressing.

I grieve when I witness what poor people are forced to endure be-cause of their lack of access to adequate healthcare. An undocumented

Salvadoran woman, a guest at the Los Angeles Catholic Worker House, had waited for four months for an appointment with her doctor for follow-up care after open-heart surgery. One day when she was suffering chest pains, I accompanied her to the local health clinic for an eleven o'clock appointment. We spent a long day in a crowded waiting area where a P.A. system, loud but barely audible, called patients not by name but by number. I checked with nursing staff several times to make sure I hadn't missed her number. At five, the nurses were closing the clinic. Her number had simply not come up. Only after my pleading was she finally seen, and then only by an intern who had never seen her before and knew nothing about her case.

Working at the Free Medical Clinic, I see a suffering among the poor that goes deeper than the physical – the feeling of shame and disgrace that so often accompanies poverty and alienation. So, in addition to providing medical care, we hope to offer a place where people know they will be treated with dignity and respect.

I know that the training health professionals receive usually encourages them to distance themselves from people. More and more, healthcare is considered a matter for technology, clinical expertise, and specialization. I also know that the high-pressure demands of mainstream medicine make it difficult for nurses and doctors to offer the kind of personal care they would like to give. In the free clinic, we have no choice but to be close to the people. We cannot help but be involved in their lives. Lacking sophisticated machines and elaborate, expensive procedures, we have little to offer but bandages and medicines, rides to appointments, and ourselves – our presence.

Though we are often overwhelmed with the sufferings of our brothers and sisters, anguished at the injustice of the system that crushes them, we try to present to them the spirit of Jesus. Those who come to the clinic offer us, in return, their presence – and with it, a tremendous grace, revealing to me the beauty of all persons and the great mystery of the love of Christ.

John McNeill writes in Taking a Chance on God, "If we can find another human being to descend with us into our private hell of powerlessness, pain, despair, and grief, then we are not alone and there

is ground for hope."[1] As we come together in the very public hell
beneath the El, we find that solid ground of hope – for all of us.

*Johanna Berrigan, PA-C, specializes in Infectious Disease. Ms.
Berrigan is affiliated with Hahnemann University Hospital and
Thomas Jefferson University Hospital. She also serves as the co-
director of the Catholic Worker Free Clinic in Catholic Workers Free
Health Clinic in the Kensington area of Philadelphia. This underserved area is known for its prevalent homeless population. The
Catholic Workers Free Health Clinic evaluates patients with a variety
of health problems with the goal of meeting the need for periodic
health care for individuals who are typically homeless, underinsured,
or uninsured.*

THE TRULY WORTHY POOR

Bob Lupton

People with a heart to assist those in need want to be assured that
their investment is used wisely. I certainly do. I don't want my alms
squandered by the irresponsible or unethical. Since I am a Christian
community developer, I am often in the position to determine who
will or will not be given aid. I've attempted to establish a set of criteria by which to judge the worthiness of a potential recipient.

A truly worthy poor senior citizen:
Is a widow above sixty-five years of age, living alone in substandard
housing, does not have a family or any relatives to care for her, has
no savings, is disabled and cannot work, exists off her monthly Social Security check, is a woman of prayer and faith, trusts God to
meet her needs, never asks anyone for help but graciously accepts
what people bring to her, and is not cranky.

A truly worthy poor family:
Is devout and close-knit, has a working father who holds down two
minimum wage jobs, has a stay-at-home mother who makes the kids
obey, washes clothes by hand and does not buy junk food, lives in
over-crowded housing, will not accept welfare, always pays bills on

time, has no automobile but is always punctual, and kids do not cuss
nor tell lies.

A truly worthy poor adult male:
Is a young man, out of school, not living off his mother, is unem-
ployed but is diligently applying for jobs every day, accepts gratefully
any kind of work for any pay offered, doesn't smoke or drink, doesn't
use drugs, attends church regularly, is not manipulative, is morally
pure, wears freshly-pressed clothes (belted at waistline), has pride in
himself, and is always clean-shaven.

A truly worthy poor adult female:
Is a young mother in public housing (only temporarily), has illegiti-
mate children conceived prior to becoming a Christian, is now celi-
bate, tithes her welfare checks and food stamps, is a high-school
dropout but manages her finances well, reads books to her children
and limits their TV watching to educational programs, prepares nutri-
tious meals, walks everywhere to save on bus fare, keeps her apartment spotless, insists on volunteering in exchange for food at the
church food-pantry, and will not accept cash from family or friends
– therefore not violating welfare rules.

I want to serve truly worthy poor people. The problem is, I can't
seem to find any. One of my fellow-staff workers thought she re-
called seeing one of them back in the early 1980s, but couldn't
remember for sure. She also reminded me that to be truly poor probably meant that one was desperate, clutching at every straw, impatient, scheming, obsessed with immediate needs, and with little drive
left for future planning. But truly worthy? Is any one of us, after all,
truly worthy? As Matthew 22:8 tells us, "The wedding feast is ready,
but those who are invited aren't worthy." May we remember Jesus'
merciful, gracious, loving words, for only he is truly worthy.

Bob Lupton has invested 40 years of his life in inner-city Atlanta. His life's work has been the rebuilding of urban neighborhoods where families can flourish and children can grow into healthy adults. Bob is the author of numerous books including Theirs Is The Kingdom; Return Flight; Renewing the City; Compassion, Justice and the Christian Life; and Toxic Charity. Bob has a PhD in psychology from the University of Georgia. He serves as a speaker, strategist, and inspirer with those who seek to establish God's shalom in the city.

THE BIBLICAL MANDATE

CHAPTER 5

BIBLICAL FOUNDATIONS FOR EMPOWERING THE POOR

Ron Sider

I know a girl named Sonya. She was born in Central America, where many children die of starvation, malnutrition, and related diseases before they are six. Sonya is my adopted daughter. She isn't among those dead children – but she could have been.

Over thirty million people in this world will die of starvation this year. In contrast, you and I live in incredible affluence. This forces us to ask some questions: What does it mean to live in great abundance while so many have so little? What does God's Word say to us?

I want to focus on two Biblical themes in addressing those questions.

The first theme is that God is on the side of the poor.
God is not biased, but if you examine certain moments in history, we see that God acts to liberate the poor and oppressed. Take the Exodus account, when God kept his promise to Abraham and called the Israelites out of oppression. The Scriptures say, "I have observed the misery of my people who are in Egypt; I have heard the cry on account of their taskmasters. Indeed, I have known their sufferings, and

I have come down to deliver them from the Egyptians."[1]

God intervened in history with the destruction of Israel and Judah. The explosive message of the prophet is that God destroyed those nations for their idolatry and economic oppression of the poor.

When Jesus preached his inaugural sermon, he proclaimed, "The Spirit of the Lord is upon me, because he has anointed me to bring good news to the poor. He has sent me to proclaim release to the captives and recovery of sight to the blind, to let the oppressed go free, to proclaim the year of the Lord's favor."[2]

During his ministry, Jesus healed the sick and the blind, fed the hungry, and warned his followers in the strongest possible terms that they must follow in his steps. At the supreme moment in history when God became flesh, the God of the Exodus was still at work, acting to lift up the poor, the weak, and the marginalized. This is why I say God has a special concern for the poor.

The Bible goes further and says that God works in history to lift up the poor and the oppressed, and cast down the rich and powerful. In the Magnificat, Mary states, "He has brought down the powerful from their thrones, and lifted up the lowly; he has filled the hungry with good things, and sent the rich away empty."[3] James 5:1 reads, "Come now, you rich people, weep and wail for the miseries that are coming to you."[4] The Bible tells us that the wealthy sometimes get rich by oppression, or they are rich and fail to share. God is displeased with both of these. James goes on to warn, "You have laid up treasures for the last days. Listen! The wages of the laborers who mowed your fields, which you kept back by fraud, cry out, and the cries of the harvesters have reached the ears of the Lord of Hosts. You have lived on the earth in luxury and in pleasure." God hates and punishes neglect of the poor.

Jeremiah clearly saw that sometimes people get rich and powerful through oppression. He says, "Scoundrels are found among my people; they take over the goods of others. Like fowlers they set a trap; they catch human beings. Like a cage full of birds, their houses are full of treachery; therefore they have become rich, they have grown fat and sleek. They know no limits in deeds of wickedness;

they do not judge with justice the cause of the orphan, to make it prosper, and they do not defend the rights of the needy."[5]

Through the prophets, God announces devastation on rich individuals and rich societies that oppress the poor. We read in Isaiah, "The Lord enters into judgment with the elders and princes of his people: 'It is you who have devoured the vineyard; the spoil of the poor is in your houses. What do you mean by crushing my people, by grinding the face of the poor?'"[6] God is at work in history, lifting up the poor and the browbeaten, and casting down the wealthy who get rich by oppression, or those who are rich and fail to share.

The Bible goes so far as to say that the people of God are not really the people of God if they do not care about the poor like God does. It doesn't matter how orthodox our creed, how intense our charismatic prayer meetings, or how proper our liturgies; if we don't share God's concern for the poor, then we are simply not God's people. The prophets state that you cannot worship God and mistreat the poor. Amos proclaims, "I hate, I despise your festivals; and I take no delight in your solemn assemblies. Even though you offer me your burnt offerings and grain offerings, I will not accept them."[7] Amos also accuses them of bribing judges so that the poor couldn't get a fair deal in the courts, so that they could trick the poor and take their land.[8] God desires justice, not only religious ritual.

Jesus said the same thing. He said that those who don't feed the hungry, clothe the naked, and care for the sick will go to hell.[9] That is strong language! John says it differently: "How does God's love abide in anyone who has the world's good and sees a brother or sister in need yet refuses to help?"[10] These texts seem to say that regardless of any religious experience we may claim, affluent people who neglect the poor are not the people of God at all.

It is central to our faith that we are sinful creatures who can stand before God only because Jesus died for us on the cross. Nevertheless, we cannot therefore ignore the call to care for the poor. John Calvin pointedly said that if we claim to have a saving faith and don't do the things that people with saving faith are supposed to do according to Scripture, then there is the most severe doubt about whether we have saving faith at all. The Bible is clear – God wants his people to share his concern for the poor, the oppressed, and the marginalized.

When I say that God is on the side of the poor, I am not saying that God cares more about the poor than other people. God cares equally about everyone, while you and I care a lot more about ourselves than we do about the poor. By contrast, God seems biased because he is equally concerned with the poor.

The second Biblical theme is that when we think about poverty, we should not only think of it in individualistic terms but also in terms of structural injustice.
The institution of slavery was perfectly legal, yet it destroyed millions of people. During the eighteenth century, it was legal for Christian mine owners to employ children as young as six years old for ten to twelve hours a day. Many children died. It was perfectly legal to destroy children that way.

One of the best Philadelphia high schools in the 1950s was Northeast High. It had a great athletic tradition and a tremendous academic record. It was also almost entirely white. During the 1960s, black people began to move into that neighborhood – and white families began to move out to another all-white section of town. Eventually a new school was needed for the increased white population there. So they built the new school – and called it Northeast High School. They took the school colors, the trophies, and all the memories of academic and athletic excellence and moved them from the old school to the new school. They told the teachers that they could move as well, and two-thirds of them did. The old high school was renamed Edison High. The students were predominantly African American and Hispanic. Both the building and the academics were the pits. But Edison High holds one national record: more young people from Edison High died in Vietnam than from any other high school in the United States.[11]

Who is responsible for this? The mayor and the school board certainly knew what they were doing. The Christian parents who sent their children to the new school certainly knew a little bit about what was happening. The future job prospects of those white students were in part possible because of the poor education that was left behind for blacks and Hispanics at Edison High. This raises a difficult question: do we sin if we participate in a system that is unfair?

There are some in the church who have mastered social sins. There are others who have an expertise in personal sins – lying, stealing, and committing adultery. The interesting thing is that the Bible seems to care very much about both. The prophet Amos put it this way: "For three transgressions of Israel and for four, I will not revoke the punishment; because they sell the righteous for silver, and the needy for a pair of sandals."[12]

Bible scholars tell us that apparently the rich had arranged with the judges to use a legal technicality to trick the poor, take their land, and sell them into slavery. "They trample the head of the poor into the dust of the earth, and push the afflicted out of the way." Amos was talking about economic oppression and how God is going to punish it, but he goes on to say, "Father and son go into the same girl, so that my holy name is profaned."[13] In one breath, the prophet condemns both economic oppression and sexual sin.

The Bible goes so far as to say that the people of God are not really the people of God if they do not care about the poor like God does.

Laws themselves can be unjust. The Psalmist asks, "Can wicked rulers be allied with you, those who contrive mischief by statute?"[14] Isaiah proclaimed, "Ah, you who make iniquitous decrees, who write oppressive statutes, to turn aside the needy from justice and to rob the poor of their right."[15] In other words, woe to the legislators who write unjust laws, and the bureaucrats who carry them out.

Social sins are so subtle that we can almost be involved without knowing it. Some of the nastiest words in the Bible were spoken by the prophet Amos against the cultured, upper-class women of his day. He says, "Hear this word, you cows of Bashan who are on the Mount Samaria…" That is certainly not the way you win friends and influence people on Society Hill! He goes on to say, "…who oppress the poor, who crush the needy, who say to their husbands, 'Bring something to drink!'"[16] The women are telling their husbands that they need a little more money to keep up with the Joneses or perhaps go one up on them. Amos declares, "The Lord God has sworn by his holiness: The time is surely coming upon you, when they shall take you away with hooks, even the last one of you with fishhooks."

The women to whom Amos spoke probably had little contact with poor peasants. They probably didn't realize that their gorgeous clothes and spirited parties were possible because of the oppression of the poor. Perhaps they were kind to an occasional peasant, giving away Thanksgiving baskets each year. But Amos called these privileged women "cows" because they were a part of a social system that was unfair. The text makes it clear that if we are members of a privileged group, if we profit from a social structure that is unfair, and do not try to change it, then we stand under God's judgment.

I have focused on two Biblical themes: the first is that God has a powerful concern for the poor; the second is that when dealing with poverty, it is essential to address the structural injustice in our society. These themes help focus our concern for the poor, but they don't tell us what we're supposed to do. We are left with some additional questions: What kind of structural changes should we make, and what kinds of structural changes would empower the poor? I'm not going to give a detailed answer to either question, but I want to focus on two more Biblical themes that can help us.

The Bible points us away from great extremes of wealth and poverty.
It may be that sinful people naturally develop great extremes between rich and poor, but we see in the Scriptures that God wants a different economic relationship among his people. After the Promised Land had been divided among the tribes and every family had the means to earn their way, God added an interesting provision to the Law – the Jubilee.[17] Every fifty years, all land was to return to its original owner without compensation. In addition, every seven years, all debts were to be cancelled.[18] Both of these measures were divinely

willed mechanisms to prevent greater and greater extremes between the rich and the poor.

Concern for redeemed economic relationship didn't end in the Old Testament. Jesus spoke about how his followers would share with the poor. Filled with the Spirit, the early church began to do that in incredible ways, so that there was not a needy person among them.[19] Paul, the great missionary to the Gentiles, considered economic fellowship in the body of believers so important that he devoted months of potential preaching time collecting an intercontinental offering from Greek-speaking Europeans for Aramaic-speaking Asian Christians. In his appeal he says, "I do not mean that there should be relief for others and pressure on you, but it is a question of a fair balance between your present abundance and their need, so that their abundance may be for your need, in order that there may be a fair balance."[20]

I don't think that God is demanding an absolute equality of consumption, but these texts point us away from great extremes of wealth and poverty. God revealed these norms in Scriptures because God knew how we were made, and that if we were to live in this manner, society would be made whole.

The Biblical doctrine of sin helps us understand why these guidelines are important. Wealth is power, and power is dangerous. Power is not necessarily evil, but it is dangerous. Because of the Fall, power tends to corrupt. Sinful, selfish people cannot be trusted to use great economic power for the common good rather than themselves.

I do not mean that we are stealing from someone else when we create wealth. The Biblical doctrine of work affirms the goodness and importance of the creation of wealth. The Scripture also affirms the significance of private property. Jesus apparently assumed that this was legitimate, since he gave commands to give to the poor and loan to the poor – which wouldn't make sense if we didn't have anything to give!

While the Bible affirms the value of private property, however, it totally rejects the notion of absolute, private ownership.[21] There is only one absolute owner in the Bible – and that is God. As Lord of all things, God possesses unconditional property rights. The psalmist declares, "The earth is the Lord's and all that is in it."[22] Since God is the absolute owner, God can insist on the right of all to have land they need to earn a living. God says that this is a higher right than the notion of unlimited, absolute private ownership. God demands that Israel have a Jubilee every fifty years. "The land must not be sold in perpetuity, for the land is mine; with me you are but aliens and tenants."[23]

> **We have allowed our affluent, materialistic society to determine how we relate to the poor rather than allowing Biblical teaching on economics to direct our lives.**

Between one Jubilee and the next, if a poor man sold his land and later got back on his feet and wanted to buy back his land, the new owner would have to sell it back. The first person's right to have the land to earn his own way is a higher right than the new owner's right to make a profit off the land. The Bible challenges absolute property rights and any system that makes maximizing profits its idol.

The Bible also challenges centrally planned and state-owned economies, both of which trend toward totalitarianism. There is no suggestion in the Scriptures of a massive welfare system that creates dependence. The year of Jubilee called for the redistribution of land, the basic unit of production, in order to promote strong families being able to earn their own way. If Israel had followed the law about Jubilee, it would have promoted a decentralized form of limited, private ownership where everybody had the economic resources to shape their own lives.

Decentralized, limited private ownership rather than state ownership is important for two reasons. On the positive side, the Biblical doctrine of creation summons each person to be a co-worker with God; we are to exercise dominion over the earth, shape history, and influence the decisions that affect our lives. If economic power is centralized in state ownership, people become cogs in complex, economic machines and are not able to affect the crucial decisions that shape their lives. On the negative side, we have the tendency toward corruption. In a fallen world, state ownership is almost certain to lead to totalitarianism, as we have seen in Eastern European and Soviet societies.

One thing that strikes me as ironic is that people who vigorously oppose centralized economies in communist societies frequently fail to apply these principles to Western societies. Multinational corporations have immense economic and political power. In our own country, the power of the largest five hundred companies is so great that genuine democracy is threatened. A Biblically-informed fear of concentrated power will not only rejoice in the current movement toward decentralized economic and political power in communist societies but also demand application of the same principles in our own country.

I have tried to develop four Biblical principles: 1) God is on the side of the poor, 2) sin is both personal and social, 3) we should not have great extremes of both wealth and poverty, and 4) God will form a decentralized power economic order. It's clear that the Bible says a lot about these topics – in fact, there are more texts about God's concern for the poor than there are on the resurrection. I think that the bodily resurrection of Jesus is absolutely central to Biblical faith, but if centrality in Scripture is any clue to what you and I should consider important, then we should take God's concern for the poor very seriously.

We have allowed our affluent, materialistic society to determine how we relate to the poor rather than allowing Biblical teaching on economics to direct our lives. If we are serious about the authority of the Scripture, we will let what the Bible says about God's concern for the poor be just as important in our lives as it is in the Bible.

As we examine how we should relate to the poor, we need to be careful not to latch on to simplistic answers. There are many causes of poverty. Some poverty is caused by laziness, some by poor decisions about drugs and alcohol. The proper response to both of these is evangelism.

Some poverty is caused by worldviews that do not create and

promote a proper relationship to the external order. Hinduism teaches that "untouchables" are at the bottom of society because they made sinful choices in a previous incarnation. It teaches that if people accept their lot in life, they may have a better chance for better things in the next incarnation. This becomes a rationalization for the self-interest of the powerful, similar to the one that was used in this country during the days of slavery. The response again is evangelism. A Biblical worldview needs to be shared.

Some poverty is caused by natural disasters – floods and earthquakes. When disasters happen, we need to provide relief as fast as we can.

Some poverty is caused by a lack of appropriate technology – people don't have the proper tools to create wealth and earn their own way. Thank God for christian development organizations digging wells, helping with better seeds, and empowering people to stand on their own two feet. In order to further this work, we need to live more simply in our personal lives "so that others may simply live."[24] We can decide to spend less on ourselves, drive a smaller car, and keep it for a few years, not keep up with clothing fashions, and in a dozen different ways spend less on ourselves so that we can share more with others.

In the same way, our congregations need to be living witnesses that we worship the God of the poor. Several years ago, a church in the Midwest was embarking on a major building program when they heard that an earthquake had destroyed several churches in Guatemala. When they came together to vote on their new building plans, someone said, "How can we go ahead with our ecclesiastical Cadillac when our brothers in Guatemala have just lost their Volkswagen?" That was so disrupting that they decided to send a few people to Guatemala to investigate. When that congregation understood the need, they slashed their building program by two-thirds. They sent over half of the money they saved to Guatemala and used it to rebuild twenty-five churches and twenty-eight pastors' homes.

So far I have mentioned several causes of poverty – laziness, worldviews, natural disasters, and the lack of appropriate technology. There is also structural injustice. American pineapple companies in Hawaii were confronted with a labor union that was demanding a decent wage for its workers, so they moved to the Philippines.[25] There President Marcos kept the unions from developing any power by torturing and imprisoning people. With the very low wages in the Philippines, profits were high. But workers could not adequately provide for their families, and many children died from inadequate nutrition and healthcare. Who was responsible for these dying children? Was Mr. Marcos responsible? Yes. Were the American corporations responsible? I think so. Some of that pineapple is in our refrigerators. Are you and I responsible? To some extent, we are a part of these unjust systems. We need to face that fact and find appropriate ways to respond to the aspect of poverty caused by unjust structures.

Someone has said that if you give a person a fish, you feed that person for a day, but if you teach that person to fish, that person can eat for a lifetime. That is community development. Unfortunately, so many of the fishponds of our world are owned by a tiny, wealthy elite, or by multinational corporations. If people are going to be able to earn their own way, we have got to make political and economic changes so that the poor can have a share in the fishponds – precisely so they can earn their own way.

In Sri Lanka, they used to have dreadful problems with malaria. Then they sprayed the marshes – breeding ground for mosquitos spreading malaria. In three years, the death rate was cut by as much as Western Europe had cut the death rate in three hundred years.[26] They used a structural approach to prevent disease. I would submit that their approach was more Biblical than praying for the sick or building hospitals. I believe in divine healing today, and I thank God for hospitals, but we need to begin to address the structural roots of poverty.

While in India several years ago, I met an Indian bishop who told me a story to underline the importance of a structural approach. He told me of a psychiatric asylum that had an interesting way of deciding whether a person was well enough to go home. They would give a person a spoon and tell him or her to empty the tub. If the person started dipping the water out one spoonful at a time, without turning the tap off, they knew the person was not well enough to go home.

This is the way most of us deal with poverty – one person (spoonful) at a time. Certainly, we should give Thanksgiving baskets to families lacking food or dig wells when people do not have access to clean water. But when we can get to the structural root of the problem that makes people poor, we should work on that. This takes some organization, and may mean that we get politically involved. We need to change our personal lives, change the church, and change the larger society.

What are you looking for in life? As we look around, it seems that our preoccupation is with affluence, wealth, and security. We want nice cars, grand houses, and all the gadgets that modern technology makes available. Is that what you really want in life? In a world where two billion people have never heard of Jesus Christ, we American Christians spend four times as much on weight reduction programs as we do on missions. In a world where one billion people have no education, no healthcare, no housing, and in many cases, not even enough food, do we really want to settle into an uncaring affluence and let the rest of the world rot?

Jesus invites us to a more risky, more costly way. He calls us to give our lives for others, spreading the gospel and seeking justice in the inner cities of America, in the villages and slums of the Third World, in the halls of government, and in the corporate boardrooms. At the end of his earthly ministry, Jesus said, "Unless a grain of wheat falls into the earth and dies, it remains a single grain; but if it dies, it bears much fruit. Those who love their life lose it, and those who hate their life in this world will keep it for eternal life. Whoever serves me must follow me."[27]

Will we follow Jesus in his concern for the poor?

Dr. Ron Sider, a Senior Distinguished Professor of Theology, Holistic Ministry & Public Policy at Palmer Theological Seminary, is also President Emeritus of Evangelicals for Social Action, an organization that he helped start in the 1970s, inspiring a historic movement of christians to see the peace-and-justice dimension of their biblical beliefs. Dr. Sider received a B.A. from Waterloo Lutheran University, an M.A. (history) from Yale University, a B.D. from Yale Divinity School, and a Ph.D. (history) from Yale University.

Ron Sider is known worldwide for providing leadership to the movement of evangelicals who recognize not just the spiritual, but also the social and political implications of a high view of Scripture. His book Rich Christians in an Age of Hunger *was lauded by* Christianity Today *as being among the top 100 books in religion in the 20th century and the seventh most influential book in the evangelical world in the last 50 years.*

CHAPTER 6

MEDICINE AS MINISTRY WITH THE POOR

Nathan Cook

As a high school senior, I was a semifinalist for a full tuition ministry scholarship at a prominent Christian college. My final interview with the scholarship committee was going better than I had imagined until they asked their final question, "Is there anything other than full time ministry that you can possibly see yourself doing?"

"Yes," I responded, "I want to come to this school because it has both a great religion department and a great pre-med program. Both of my parents have taught basic sciences in university settings and I have considered practicing medicine."

The excitement that had built in the room over our previous discussions of ministry deflated. I didn't get the scholarship.

Reflecting on that experience now, our preconceived notions of what constituted fulltime ministry was shortsighted. Neither the scholarship committee nor I could conceive of physicians engaged in round-the-clock ministry, yet that is exactly what the Christian Community Health Fellowship promotes. CCHF encourages and equips medical professionals to sacrificially provide healthcare to the poor in the name of Jesus Christ. Should healthcare for the poor be seen as a ministry of the church? Is it a Biblical concept?

In Luke 16:19-31, Jesus tells the story of a rich man who lived in luxury. A diseased homeless man named Lazarus lay at his doorstep begging for scraps of food from the rich man's table. Lazarus' only comfort came from stray dogs that licked his wounds. Both men die. In Paradise, Lazarus is comforted in the arms of Abraham. The rich man suffers the torture of hell. The rich man pleads with Abraham to allow Lazarus to bring him a glass of water to relieve his suffering. When Abraham refuses, the rich man pleads on behalf of his wealthy family members, "Send him to my father's house. For I have five brothers, and I want him to warn them about this place of torment so they won't have to come here when they die."

Abraham responds, "Moses and the prophets have warned them. Your brothers can read their writings anytime that they want."

The rich man, now cognizant of his family's greed, pleads again, "No, Father Abraham! But if someone is sent to them from the dead, then they will turn from their sins." Abraham closes the story with this final statement, "If they won't listen to Moses and the prophets, they won't listen even if someone rises from the dead."

In his lifetime, the rich man failed to comfort Lazarus in his affliction. Daily, he ignored the plight of the poor at his doorstep. He lived in luxury while poor Lazarus suffered from disease, open wounds, and malnourishment. The rich man had the material resources at his disposal to comfort Lazarus in his affliction but chose not to do so. He ignored the teachings of the law and the prophets.

"If there are any poor people in your towns when you arrive in the land the Lord your God is giving you, do not be hard-hearted or tightfisted toward them. Instead, be generous and lend them whatever they need… If you refuse to make the loan and the needy person cries out to the Lord, you will be considered guilty of sin. Give freely without begrudging it, and the Lord your God will bless you in everything you do. There will always be some among you who are poor. That is why I am commanding you to share your resources freely with the poor and with other Israelites in need."[1]

By refusing to help the poor man at his doorstep, the rich man's

heart was hardened by greed. God's law promoted grace and generosity toward the poor. The rich man failed to obey God's law and
was guilty of sin. The warning from the prophets is just as explicit.

"Son of man, prophesy against the shepherds, the leaders of
Israel. Give them this message from the Sovereign Lord: Destruction
is certain for you shepherds who feed yourselves instead of your
flocks. Shouldn't shepherds
feed their sheep? You drink
the milk, wear the wool, and
butcher the best animals, but
you let your flocks starve.
You have not taken care
of the weak. You have not
tended the sick or bound up

> *The word "compassion"
> literally means "to suffer
> with." Are we willing to enter
> into Lazarus' suffering, or will
> we, like the rich man, ignore
> the poor man at our gate?*

the broken bones. You have not gone looking for those who have
wandered away and are lost. Instead, you have ruled them with force
and cruelty."[2]

Just as the religious leaders of Ezekiel's day failed to tend to the
sick, bind broken bones, and feed those who were starving, the rich
man ignored the plight of his poor neighbor, choosing to live a luxu-
rious life while Lazarus suffered. Lazarus needed proper medical
attention. Ezekiel explicitly states that caring for the sick and wounded is the responsibility of God's people. If nothing else, God's final
words of promise and judgment in Ezekiel 34:16 should have
snapped the rich man and his family to their senses. "I will search for
my lost ones who strayed away, and I will bind up the injured and
strengthen the weak. But I will destroy those who are fat and powerful. I will feed them. Yes – feed them justice!"

This is the real question that Jesus poses to his audience through
the story of the rich man and Lazarus, "Will we be like the rich man
who turns a blind eye to the needs of the poor or will we use the
talents and resources that God has blessed us with to demonstrate his
compassion and grace?" The word "compassion" literally means "to
suffer with." Are we willing to enter into Lazarus' suffering, or will
we, like the rich man, ignore the poor man at our gate? Will we be

moved by the unmerited favor we have received from Jesus through the forgiveness of our own sins? Having received God's free and unmerited favor, will we bless others with medical care, even those whom we perceive as unworthy, as a demonstration of the gospel?

Over the past decade I have watched hundreds of medical students wrestle with these concepts. Medical practice promises a comfortable, if not immoderate, lifestyle. While many enter medical school seeking to serve God through medicine, lifestyle choices often derail students from pursuing medicine as a ministry and calling. The grueling nature of residency helps students to justify the promise of an abundant lifestyle as a just reward for the hardships they endure. The drift from medicine as ministry to medicine as a means to securing comfort in life can be slow and methodical. Other times it can be in your face. A friend of mine was invited to a party at her instructor's house following her graduation from medical school. She arrived at the house with several other friends. When her instructor opened the door to her lavish estate the medical students were greeted with the following worldly words of affirmation, "This is it, ladies, this is what you have all been working for!" The promise of luxury is alluring, but it is to our detriment. It should never be the driver of our decisions. The story of the rich man should serve as a warning. God has given us responsibility to care for the poor as a demonstration of his compassion and grace. Healing originates in God. We are called to be conduits of his grace in the world.

Jesus provides medical ministers with another positive example to follow in the story of the Good Samaritan. Jesus is asked by a religious expert, "What must I do to receive eternal life?" Jesus replies, "What does the law of Moses say?" The man answered, "You must love the Lord your God with all your heart, all your soul, all your strength, and all your mind. And love your neighbor as yourself." "Right," Jesus said, "Do this and you will live!" The man wanted to justify his actions so he asked Jesus another question, "And who is my neighbor?" Jesus responds with the familiar story of the Good Samaritan as an example of one who loved his neighbor well.[3]

Like the story of the rich man and Lazarus, the story of the Good

Samaritan opens with a man in distress. A Jewish traveler has been beaten and robbed by bandits, left penniless, naked and half dead on the side of the road. Like the rich man and the religious leaders of Ezekiel's day, the religious leaders in Jesus' story fail to act on behalf of the traveler in distress. The Samaritan man, however, sees the man's plight and is moved by compassion to help him. Again we see compassion as the primary motivator. The Samaritan stops and enters into the man's distress. He soothes the man's wounds with medicine and bandages them. Not only does the Samaritan triage the victim, he also provides prolonged hospice care, at his own expense. The Samaritan's actions are a clear demonstration of the gospel. Just as Jesus entered into the suffering of a fallen and broken world to heal and save those who were estranged from God at the cost of his own life, the Samaritan enters into the life of the Jewish traveler, bandages his wounds and provides for his recovery at an inn, at great cost to himself. The Good Samaritan lavishly loves a stranger in need of medical attention.

Jesus concludes the story with a question of his own, "Which of these three would you say was a neighbor to the man who was attacked by bandits?"

"The one who showed him mercy," the man replied.

Then Jesus said, "Yes, now go and do the same."

To what extent are we as Christians in the medical community demonstrating the gospel of Jesus Christ? Are we like the Samaritan, motivated by compassion and sacrificial love to provide healthcare for the poor at our own expense? Will we be faithful to Jesus' command to go and do likewise, demonstrating mercy through our churches, clinics, and communities?

How do we practically apply these lessons to the practice of medicine? Do these stories inform a response to the current debate on health reform? Or should we, the church, stay out of the debate altogether? I certainly don't have the stomach for debate. Despite my own inclination toward avoidance, I recognize that the Biblical perspective is not the only perspective that shapes the way we practice medicine. All of us are working out our calling to serve God as ministers of medicine in a world of competing perspectives.

At the writing of this article, America is wrestling through the implementation or rejection of aspects of the Affordable Care Act including Medicaid expansion. While many states have decided to expand Medicaid, in my home state of Tennessee the debate is far from over.

"Medicaid expansion would have been financially unsustainable in the long run. The program would have covered mostly male, able-bodied, childless adults making one hundred and thirty-eight percent of the federal poverty level or less. Only sixteen percent of these individuals work fulltime, year-round. We should be focused on reducing unemployment for this population, not reducing the incentive to find work."

My friend's conclusion is based on his own perception of personal responsibility. In his view, it is the responsibility of the individual to work for and to earn healthcare benefits. Again, in his view, when individuals fail to be personally responsible, they create an unjustified fiscal burden on taxpayers.

The teachings of the law and the prophets, and Jesus' examples of the rich man and the Good Samaritan point us to a different starting place in the debate. Instead of assessing if an individual is worthy of our help, the Biblical passages teach us to open our eyes and witness our neighbor's plight. For Jesus, the poor are not a faceless crowd, depleting the resources of the wealthy. Jesus gives the poor man a name, Lazarus, and a face, the man outside your door. For followers of Jesus, poverty must be personal to inspire the compassion we need to overcome our tight-fistedness. Jesus uses compassion to help us enter, in an incarnational way, into our neighbor's suffering. Through his stories, Jesus compels us to open our door or to cross the street in order to physically enter into space occupied by the poor. Then like Abraham, we welcome them into our space, providing comfort through an embrace, or like the Good Samaritan, we bandage the wounded traveler, place them in our car, drive them to the hospital, and pay their bill at our own expense. Can there be a clearer demonstration of the gospel than paying an exorbitant hospital bill for a man who doesn't deserve it?

If compassion is not our first response to seeing the suffering of others, we can soften our hearts by recalling God's command to care for the poor, and God's judgment for those who fail to do so. Or we can remember a time we received God's grace despite our own sin and disobedience. Drawing from these memories, we provide grace to others because we have first received grace from God. "He comforts us in all our troubles so that we can comfort others. When others are troubled, we will be able to give them the same comfort God has given us."[4]

The church can and should be the starting place for reforming healthcare to meet the needs of the poor.

If we still need help conceptualizing what medical ministry with the poor can look like, there is a great example from church history that complements these Biblical narratives. St. Basil the Great was the son of a wealthy lawyer, a prominent theologian, and a leader of the early church. He had a vision for an ideal Christian community called The New City. Its centerpiece was a hospital called the Basiliad. Using his own financial resources, money from the church, donations gathered from the private sector through St. Gregory of Nazianzus' preaching "On Love for the Poor," and funding from Emperor Valens, the hospital was built. The church, government, and philanthropic community pulled together for the benefit of those who were sick and downcast. Medical personnel, monks and nuns, and the involuntary poor lived together in The New City mutually benefiting from one another. In addition to healthcare provided by the medical professionals, the monks and nuns taught the poor basic trades that would help them benefit from and contribute to the larger economy. The community pulled together to meet each other's physical, emotional, and spiritual needs. Thirty years later, the success of the Basiliad led John Chrysostom to build several hospitals using the same model. The church led the way in health reform seventeen hundred years ago.[5] Can we do so again today?

Our original question was "Should healthcare for the poor be seen as a ministry of the church?"

The answer, I think, is an unequivocal "Yes."

God commands that we care for the poor in the Torah, and specifically mentions through Ezekiel that we attend to their medical needs. Jesus affirms the teachings of the law and the prophets through the stories of Lazarus and the Good Samaritan. The early church modeled for us what holistic care with the poor can look like. We have clear principles from Scripture that compel us to enter into the lives of the poor and allow them to enter into our lives so that we might share the love, compassion, and sacrifice of Jesus with one another. Now more than ever, we need the St. Basils of today to lead with vision, demonstrating to the broader culture what healthcare in God's kingdom should look like. The church can and should be the starting place for reforming healthcare to meet the needs of the poor. Equipped with Biblical teaching and empowered by the Holy Spirit, will you lead the way?

Nathan Cook, MDiv, is the Spiritual Director at Resurrection Health Family Medicine Residency in Memphis, TN. A graduate of Asbury Seminary, Nathan is an elder and co-founder of a network of house churches in the inner city of Memphis. A former HIV program manager for Christ Community Health Services and executive director of Christ Community Ministries, Nathan currently serves as spiritual health director for Resurrection Health. Nathan has a beautiful wife, Kim, and three young children, Caleb, Grace, and Ella.

CHAPTER

7

THE STATUS AND WORTH OF WOMEN:
A BIBLICAL PERSPECTIVE

Irene Schomus Morrow

"My husband just lost his job. Would you pray for our family?"
asked Ruby, a woman at a local Bible study. A mother of nine, with
four children under the age of three, Ruby has known poverty all of
her life. A Christian only a few months, she looks to Jesus for hope
in seemingly hopeless circumstances. Being poor and black, she is
on the bottom of both the economic and racial pecking orders. And
being a woman seems to make things worse. The pressures of child-
care and managing a home without an income make life a constant
struggle. Issues such as "equal pay for equal work" are not even
relevant in the face of so many basic concerns.

As if trying to break out of the poverty cycle weren't enough,
women typically face a number of struggles in the workplace. In
the healthcare system, this is particularly true. If a woman is trained
for nursing, she can expect to face an almost systematic tenseness
between female nurses and usually male physicians. If she becomes
a physician, she can expect to feel pressure from society and almost

equal pressure not to interrupt her career. If she marries a physician, administrator, or researcher, she may struggle with whether she has an identity separate from her husband or children. No matter which of these options she chooses, she can expect to receive less pay and fewer opportunities for advancement than the men with whom she works.

We face these problems, in various forms, as women and health-care professionals. The problems are not unique to the poor, but they are intensified, as women have to cope with economic struggles and breaking the poverty cycle. As a Christian health worker in a poor community, I am committed to discipleship as a foundation for individual and community development. As I have grown closer to the women I serve, I see the weight of oppression they are under. Some women tell me how their husbands frequently drink and gamble away the meager family income and often physically abuse them. The church should be a solace for such women, but too often it is not. One friend relayed how her pastor frequently preaches on the need to keep a woman in her place, referring to her as a "big child in the home." Often essential discipleship issues are bypassed in favor of enforcing edicts such as those forbidding women to wear pants. Such oppression is by no means confined to minority struggles or to the poor.

Fairly recently, I struggled with the problem of being a female in a male-dominated workplace and church. My sense of inherent worth was shaken as I realized that my femaleness was typically viewed as a liability. Being successful in the workplace meant either being a man or acting like a man. Furthermore, the patients usually come to the clinic with the view that a male professional is more competent and trustworthy.

I looked into God's word and the church, but was initially discouraged by what I found. In Scripture, I found a book written largely by men, to men. I was commanded to do certain things in order to be strengthened in my "inner man" so that I could become a "man of God." I struggled with the conflicting messages from the workplace and the church. In the workplace, I need to be the best nurse practitioner that I can be. In the church, however, there seems to be a subtle pressure to remember that I am female first and that this fact puts a "divine limitation" on the use of my gifts.

Does God care about the unique pressures and injustices faced by women? What does God offer to women like Ruby and me to sustain our unique worth as women? We know that the Bible is filled with references to God's particular concern for the poor and oppressed and God's concern for unity and love across racial barriers. But, what does it say about God's concern for poor women who sense that their gender only adds to their powerlessness? Does God give gifts to women and then command that they not be used? Does God require that women grow into "men of God?" Does God require for women as well as for men the same dedication, preparation, and obedience in carrying out his commandments? Poor or rich, black or white, patients or providers, who are we as women in God's eyes?

In my own search to understand who I am in God's eyes, I made some exciting discoveries that deepened my acceptance of myself as God's daughter.

In my own search to understand who I am in God's eyes, I made some exciting discoveries that deepened my acceptance of myself as God's daughter. I found good news for my friends in the Bible study – and for all women. I found that the language in the English translations does not reflect the true meaning of many of the passages in Scripture. I found a positive view of women throughout Scripture and an overwhelmingly radical treatment of women by Jesus. I found women in the early church exercising their responsibilities that are often not encouraged in the church today.

First I found that some of the traditional interpretations of the passages referring to men are generally exclusionary. For example, several words translated as implying male in the English language actually mean both men and women – that is, person regardless of sex. The Greek word anthropos commonly translated "man" in English, actually means humankind, male and female. A different word, aner, was used to signify a male. Scriptures such as Romans 7:22 and Romans 3:28 are more accurately translated: For I delight in the law of God in my inmost self *and* For we hold that a person is justified by faith apart from works prescribed by the law.

In order to grasp the significance of the language issue, one writer suggests that we imagine the reverse of the present norm. Imagine that all references to men would be included in the word "woman," "sisterhood" would be used to include males as well as females in the unity of believers. Immediately we start to feel uncomfortable at such narrowness and degradation of men. It would probably encourage women to think more highly of themselves than they ought. Likewise the practice of excluding women in language is narrow and degrading. Exclusionary language in Scripture perpetuates the un-Biblical idea that a woman's identity is not important and serves to subtly reinforce a sense of worthlessness in God's female creation.

I saw that Jesus had compassion and a dignifying love for women.

Second, the Old Testament Scriptures affirm the value of women. From the beginning of creation, God revealed woman's equality with man. Genesis 1:27 says, "And God created humankind in his image, in the image of God he created them; male and female he created them." Even though Adam was created first, according to Genesis, this does not imply a higher status. If the order of creation was ascending (plants, animals, man, and woman) and if the creation order is looked at as a claim for status, it would most certainly imply that women, created last, was the crowning glory of God's achievement!

Genesis 2:20 implies that woman was created to be a "helper" for man. This idea causes a dilemma for the single woman who is not linked to a man to "help" with his ministry and for the married woman who has a call to her own ministry. But, the translation of the word "helper" is the same one that is used in reference to God helping his people. "The God of my father was my help."[1] And "Do not turn your servant away in anger, you who have been my help. Do not cast me off, do not forsake me, O God of my salvation."[2]

The word is never used to signify a subordinate position. On the contrary, it always refers to a equal or superior relationship to the one being helped. This is in contrast to the belief of some church leaders on the place of women, such as John Calvin, who stated, "The teaching of Moses is that woman was created later to be a kind of appendage to the man, on the express condition that she should be ready to obey him."[3]

Third, I saw that Jesus had compassion and a dignifying love for women. It is exciting and uplifting to see this unprecedented acceptance of women in light of the culture of his day. The world that Jesus entered was not friendly toward the female creation. In the pagan cultures many female babies never had the chance to grow up because infanticide was common, and to bear a female was considered disgraceful and a sign of failure. This was true in the Jewish culture as well. A Jewish man thanked God daily that he was not born a Gentile or a woman. Women had no part in the synagogue. They were not allowed to learn the Torah; in fact, it was considered an offense and a disgrace to teach the Torah to a woman.

So what did Jesus, a Jewish male, say to women in his day by action and words? First of all, he was born of a woman. God could have chosen to bypass the humility of birth by a woman, any woman, let alone a poor peasant girl. God could have just appeared on the earth. Instead, the God of the Universe honored women by becoming dependent on her, allowing her to nurture him in her body and at her breast.

Keeping in mind the status of women in Jesus' day, it is understandable that there were no women among the twelve apostles. Many have cited this as a reason to restrict the women's role in the church. But all the disciples were Jewish, yet leadership in the church is not restricted to those of Jewish descent. Although women were not apostles, they were certainly part of Jesus' company of followers. In fact Luke 8:1-3 gives account of several married women with households who voluntarily followed Christ around the countryside and supported him with generous financial contributions. Matthew 15:32-38 tells of the feeding of the four thousand, including women and children who had been with Jesus for three days. Nowhere do we find Jesus rebuking these women for neglecting their primary responsibility or for being "out of the home." He never mentioned roles or gave instructions applicable for women only, and he never glorified domestic tasks as "women's work." In Luke 10:41-42, Jesus supported Mary when she neglected serving and chose instead to sit at his feet just like any other disciple. He stated, "Mary has chosen the good part." In contrast to sanctifying certain tasks as "female functions" only, Jesus gave an example of servanthood that applies to men and women by taking on certain lowly tasks himself. At the Last Supper, he took on the task of a slave and washed the feet of the shocked disciples. On another occasion we see Jesus cooking breakfast for the disciples. He broke down any basis for relegating certain roles to men or women.

Jesus never put restrictions on women or used the word "subjection" in relation to women. Rather, he emphasized women's spiritual status. He shocked the outcast Samaritan women in John 4 by speaking to her in public. He then proceeded to reveal his true identity to her, making her the first individual in Scripture he told of his Messiahship. The end result was that many believed in Jesus from her testimony. By sharing the truth about himself to this woman, he conveyed his confidence in her intellectual and spiritual abilities. He emphasized the worth of Jewish women when he cured the woman who was crippled for eighteen years, referring to her as a daughter of Abraham, even though the male leaders objected.[4] It was to a woman, Martha, that he spoke the words: "I am the resurrection and the life"[5] and to women that he first appeared after rising from the dead. He later rebuked the apostles for their hardness of heart in not believing the testimony of the women regarding his resurrection.[6]

Jesus calls for justice for women. Contrary to the culture he lived in, Jesus did not view a woman's primary importance as bearing male children. A woman of that day was disgraced if she had no children. In Luke 1:25, Elizabeth expressed her joy at finally being pregnant at an old age: "This is what the Lord has done for me when he looked favorably on me and took away the disgrace I have endured among my people." Once when a woman in the crowd called out, "Blessed is the womb that bore you and the breasts that nursed you," Jesus' reply revealed a respect for the personhood of women. He said, "Blessed rather are those who hear the word of God and obey it!"[7] A woman's standard for success is not her reproductive capacity; it is the same as a man's – that is, whether or not she hears the word of God and keeps it. Again the words of Jesus are in contrast to church leaders like Martin Luther, who stated that it mattered not that woman wearied in childbirth or even died because "they were created for that function."

> *The criterion for membership in the family of God is not based on a gender or role. Rather, it is based on the will of the Father, which is the same for both males and females.*

Jesus showed compassion for the unique needs of women in his day. In Mark 5 and Matthew 9, we read of the woman who had suffered with a hemorrhage for twelve years, spending all of her money on physicians who could not cure her. According to the Law, any woman with bleeding or discharge was considered unclean and was required to go through the purification ceremony.[8] It is hard to imagine the physical and mental anguish that resulted from this affliction which caused her to be shunned and isolated for twelve years. She took a risk in the anonymity of the crowd, secretly touching Jesus' garment, knowing that by touching him she was making him unclean. Hoping for a secret cure, she must have felt fear as Jesus stopped everything and asked who had touched him. But her fear was replaced by a new sense of freedom as Jesus lovingly said, "Daughter, your faith has made you well; go in peace, and be healed of your disease."[9]

Jesus displays compassion and acceptance to outcast "sinful" women. In one instance where the religious leaders brought a woman caught "in the very act" of adultery, Jesus refused to accept their self-righteousness and sexism as they call for her stoning, for the law on which they based their accusation also required the man to be stoned.

If she was caught in the very act, why wasn't the man also brought?

Jesus answered, "Let anyone among you who is without sin be the first to throw a stone at her."[10] He broke down any basis for a double standard in regard to immorality. No man could even continue to stand in his presence. Jesus was the only one who could legitimately stone her, but instead of condemning her, he forgave her. Throughout history, women have always been the targets of "crackdowns" on prostitution and immorality when at the same time it is often men who profit most from the practice. Jesus refused to continue the double standard.

Jesus addressed other forms of oppression of women when he chastised the Pharisees for certain practices, such as "devouring widows' homes"[11] and unrestrained divorce. Men interpreted the law so that they could divorce their wives for things such as cooking the dinner wrong or for no longer being attractive to them. Many women were left destitute and outcast because of this practice. Jesus spoke up for these women and rebuked the man who oppressed them. He told them that their hearts were hard and they lacked compassion.

Jesus calls women to service. Jesus never poked fun at women but referred to womanly qualities with respect and dignity. He described God as a female householder who is seeking her lost coin.[12] He referred to himself with the analogy of a mother hen gathering her chicks. Even on the way to the cross, he showed concern for the weeping women whom he passed. He spoke about the suffering that pregnant and nursing mothers endure in times of persecution.

Finally, in Matthew 12:46-50, Jesus reveals the criteria for being part of his family. He looked out to the crowd and asked, "Who is my mother, and who are my brothers? …Whoever does the will of my Father in heaven is my brother and sister and mother." The criterion for membership in the family of God is not based on a particular gender or role. Rather, it is based on the will of the Father, which is the same for both males and females. Jesus' commands to his followers included: to seek first his kingdom, to love one another, to wash one another's feet, to go and make disciples of all nations, to teach all that he commanded, to be his witnesses even to the remotest part of the earth, and to love one's neighbor as one's self.

These commandments were given to men and women alike. Paul stated in Galatians 3:28, "There is no longer Jew or Greek, there is no longer slave or free, there is no longer male and female; for all of you are one in Christ Jesus." This oneness was beginning to be lived out in the early church. One commentator noted that women in the Book of Acts functioned as full members of the church, joined in prayer meetings, were filled with the Spirit, were involved in good works, were recipients of healing, and were held accountable for sin.

The Scriptures are clear: God does care for the needs of women. God also calls women to the same standard of accountability as men. As a coheir with Christ, she is expected to follow Jesus' commands, to fulfill the Great Commission, to do justice, to lay down her life, and to pick up her cross daily. She is never given a formula to fulfill a certain role because of her gender. This is good news to women. Women are freed in Christ from feelings of low self-worth because their basis for worth comes solely from God, not their relation or in comparison with man. Poor women have hope from the One who said, "Come to me all you that are weary and are carrying heavy burdens, and I will give you rest."[13]

Whether in the home or in the workplace, Jesus provides the foundation for liberation, equality, salvation, and fulfillment. Just treatment of both women and men is not optional, but rather, a command. In the Scriptures, and in the example of Jesus, there is good news for women.

Irene Schomus Morrow is a Registered Nurse Practitioner and Diabetes Educator working with the CVCH Diabetes and Nutrition Program. She has worked in many different areas with diverse populations. She practiced community health nursing in rural Mississippi, trained health promoters in rural El Salvador, and worked with Central American refugees in South Texas. She has worked to develop diabetes programs at Moses Lake Community Health, Samaritan Healthcare, and Central Washington Hospital.

CHAPTER

8

HOW DO YOU KEEP GOING?

Janelle Goetcheus

The following article was written by Dr. Janelle Goetcheus for
Health & Development in 1988. Some of the statistics have
changed, although most are even more dire than mentioned
in the original article. The heart and spirit that is presented
by Dr. Goetcheus in this piece are as relevant today as they
were nearly 30 years ago.

For forty-some years now, the Church of the Savior has been in
Washington, D.C., and we now have health services in various places
in the city. We also run housing ministries, employment services,
and programs for children. My own family has been here since 1976.
This is where God has called us to invest our lives.

Yet during that time, conditions in the city have gotten worse.
There is more TB and more AIDS. More hospitals are being closed to
the poor than ever before. There are fewer housing options and more
homeless people. There is more crack, more cocaine. Washington has
become the murder capital of the world.

And, of course, this suffering is not unique to Washington. In our
nation, a child is killed by gunshot every two hours. Every night,
one hundred thousand homeless children are on our streets. We build

more and more prisons, but the prisons cannot contain the hopelessness and anger of the people. One of the sisters who worked with us
has called our country the fourth world – a world in which the poor
live in the midst of a rich country.

As we answer Jesus' call to enter into the pain of the poor, we
risk being overwhelmed by these needs. Sometimes people come to
work with us, very enthusiastic, but then they become discouraged.
Often it is because they are not seeing the changes they were hoping
to see, either in oppressive systems or in people.

One of the physicians who works with us was describing how
discouraged she felt about her work with women in the shelter
because so many of the young women were returning to a life of
prostitution. Another person in our community is building single-
room-occupancy housing to provide a place to live for ninety for-
merly-homeless people in recovery. All the money has been raised
from private sources, but angry neighbors have gone to the city
council and gotten the building permits. After court action, building
has resumed, but it now appears the city will not give a certificate of
occupancy, so the building may stand empty as a monument to the
oppressive governmental system.

Sometimes we see the changes we hope for and sometimes we
don't, but no matter how much we do, there is always so much more
to be done, so much pain we can't touch. In the midst of all this pain,
how do we keep from being overwhelmed? How do we avoid burning out? How do we keep going?

Though I surely am not living them out, I am learning some
truths that keep me going.

To Keep Doing This Work, Prayer is Essential

For me, prayer is a time for being with Jesus and trying to be quiet
and listen as the Spirit prays through me. One of our disciplines in
the Church of the Savior is to spend an hour each day in prayer. But
the other hours of the day are equally important as throughout the
day we send up short prayers like "thank you" or "I am yours."

In prayer we begin to see ourselves as God sees us and not as we have always seen ourselves. We begin to know that we are indeed chosen, that we are loved. We begin to know who we really belong to and begin to listen to what we are to be about. I often think that prayer can be much more helpful than hours of therapy.

To Keep Going, I Must Be Serving From a Sense of Call

In prayer, as we learn to surrender all, to not hold back, as we seek only to do whatever it is the Lord is asking us to do, we begin to hear our own particular calls, the specific calls God gives each of us. As we encounter Jesus, he leads us to the victims of our society, those who are oppressed.

It does not come just once and not continue. God continues to call us in new ways. Sometimes it is to a major change – a new mission or a move to a new area. Sometimes God calls us in the ordinary happenings of the day. Sometimes I look back on the interruptions I've experienced through the day, that at the time seemed intrusive, and recognize that these interruptions were God's momentary call for me.

Responding to call often means letting go of some security – whatever it is that is keeping us from responding.

Call usually involves risk-taking. Our natural tendency is to work hard to secure the future for ourselves, but responding to call often means letting go of some security – whatever it is that is keeping us from responding. Letting go can be scary because we don't know what the future will hold. But in letting go, we begin to learn God's faithfulness. We experience God's dependability and come to trust God in new ways.

Paul described to the church in Corinth this process of learning to trust:

We should like you to know how serious was the trouble that came upon us in the province of Asia. The burden of it was far too heavy for us to bear, so heavy that we even despaired of life. Indeed, we felt in our hearts that we had received a death sentence. This was meant to teach us to place reliance not on ourselves, but on God who raises the dead.

Call is not static. It does not come just once and not continue. God continues to call us in new ways.

Clarity about call protects us from being overwhelmed with need because it not only guides us in what to do, but also in what not to do. We are surrounded by far more pain than we can possibly respond to. When I am obedient to the particular call God has given me, doing what little I can, I can then trust that Jesus carries all the rest of the pain that he has not called me to carry.

We can serve with joy and with the confidence that, despite all evidence to the contrary, the kingdom of God is indeed breaking in.

One final word about call:

We often tend to think that in obeying call we are making a sacrifice. When our family was considering moving into D.C. with young children, we thought of it not as sacrifice, but as a gift – not only for us, but also for our children. Sometimes a call that looks like it will involve great sacrifice and suffering may be God's way of trying to give us heaven.

What Keeps Me Going is Belonging To a Community of Christians Who are on a Similar Journey

The members of our faith community come from a variety of denominational backgrounds, but we have been brought together through obedience to a common call – to provide healthcare to the poor in Washington. I believe it is important for all of us to find that christian community in which we can share our call, where prayer and obedience to call are very natural, and where we do not have to constantly try to explain our journey to those who do not understand.

When our family was coming to D.C. in 1976, we had no particular work lined up. We didn't know what God had in mind, but we believed God had called us to come. When we tried to explain that to other Christians, we sometimes felt that they thought that we were a bit loony, and we sometimes felt a bit loony ourselves.

When you're following God into the unknown, it's so valuable to be surrounded by a community of Christians who are really expecting God's Spirit to lead, who will encourage you to hear your own call, and who will encourage you to help bring in the kingdom of God.

You also need your Christian community to hold you accountable for your own spiritual journey. One way we in the Church of the Savior are accountable for our spiritual journeys is by belonging to what we call mission groups. Each mission group is gathered around a particular call. It was one of these mission groups, for example, that started Christ House.

The mission group I am a part of now is centered around what we call table fellowship. Table fellowship is one of our worship times at Christ House where we eat and share together by candlelight.

In this little group we have a time we call inward journey where we tell about how our week has gone, how our spiritual disciplines in prayer and Scripture transpired throughout the past few days. We report our highs and lows of the week, tell how we have been good to ourselves, and share prayer concerns. Then we work on our outward mission, which for us is the table fellowship.

But the structure isn't what is most important. What is important is just being with Christians who are sharing the journey and to whom we can be accountable.

I Draw Strength from the Ministry of the Poor

Living in the midst of so much suffering, I sometimes stop to ask, "Where is the kingdom of God in all this?" And part of the answer is that I experience the kingdom by being with those who are very poor.

This past weekend in chapel, one of the men who stays with us prayed, "Lord, don't let my way get in your way."

Another man said," I am not going to let nothing come between me and my God."

We often hide and let all sorts of things come between God and ourselves. Sometimes it's things we put our security in – jobs, house, money, prestige, power. Sometimes it is our intellect or even our education that keeps us from this kind of surrender. So the poor remind me to let nothing come between me and my God, to not hide, and to be utterly dependent on God.

The poor have also helped me understand the deepest truths of the Scripture when I have missed part of it. When people first come to Christ House, they often come very broken. However, as they begin to heal physically and spiritually, they begin to lead us in our faith. Sister Mary Louise who lived with us at Christ House died this past year. Although she had a PhD in Theology, she called the poor her professors.

At Christ House when we have times of sharing around the Scripture, those who have the most profound understanding of Scripture are often not we who have formal theological training, but those poor who have been at Christ House and who share their own knowledge of Jesus.

> *The poor remind me to let nothing come between me and my God, to not hide, and to be utterly dependent on God.*

One of the people who taught us the most this past year was Robert Spence. I met Robert at the corner of 6th and K in Washington. He was standing next to a barrel in which the homeless people had built a fire to keep warm. When the medical van pulled up, he was one of those waiting to be seen. He had a blood pressure of 190/130. We wanted to take him to the hospital, but he wouldn't go. "I'm old and just waiting to die," he said. He was the same age as I was.

He agreed to come back to Christ House with us, and when he came on the nursing floor and began to undress and take off his shoes, a stench filled the whole floor. Several of the men came to me and said, "Don't put that man in my room."

Robert was with us for a while in Christ House and then moved into his own apartment. He began to learn to read and write some, and once he could read some Scripture, he would return to Christ House to co-lead a group for older homeless men, to give them hope.

This past year on a routine chest x-ray he was found to have cancer in his lungs. While he was undergoing radiation, he came back to live at Christ House. One night he called me to come quick, and I ran to his room and found that he was hemorrhaging from the lung. All I could do was hold him in my arms as he passed away quickly.

After he passed away, we put a candle beside his bed and people began to come, the other homeless men who were there, the staff, and their children. As word about his passing away spread, other folks from the neighborhood came. As we were standing outside his room, one of the nurses said to me, "Robert got it, he really got it. Sometimes I think I have, but I really don't have it. But Robert really got it."

Robert got a lot of things. He knew Jesus. He trusted Jesus. He was looking forward to going home – looking forward to that resurrection. But I think one of the greatest gifts he gave us was a sense of family. He often said I was his sister, and he meant it. He had many sisters and brothers, many nieces and nephews around the community. If we could all see each other through Robert's eyes, we would have a much better awareness of God's holy family in this kingdom.

It is the poor who have shown me the kingdom of God.

We can't meet all the needs. In fact, in our area, no matter how much we do, the needs and the suffering seem to just keep getting greater and greater. But if we will root our lives in prayer, serve while guided by a clear call, draw support and accountability from a community of Christians on a similar journey, and be open to receive the ministry of the poor among whom we serve, not only can we manage to survive in the midst of almost infinite need – we can serve with joy and with the confidence that, despite all evidence to the contrary, the kingdom of God is indeed breaking in.

Janelle Goetcheus is a family physician who has been working in DC since 1976. She is the Medical Director of Columbia Road Health Services and Christ House, where she and her husband, Alan, live. She has recently also become the Medical Director of Unity Health Care. Janelle was a plenary speaker at CCHF's first conference in Washington, DC, in 1982, as well as recently in 2014.

PERSONING THE VISIONS

CHAPTER 9

LOVE IS THE MARK

John Umhau

Becoming a physician has been something like a pilgrimage for me. This pilgrimage is a process, not a place I've arrived at, and it is a journey marked by love.

Love thy neighbor

And that love, I believe, is the mark of the Christian – or what Christian health professionals should be characterized by when attending to patients. Love can motivate us to professional excellence, to keep up with the latest medical advances, and to think carefully about the problems our patients face. Love compels us to see our patients as whole persons and to be aware of all the forces – social, psychological, spiritual, and physical – that influence their well-being. If we love someone who is in need, we naturally want to help, even if meeting that particular need is not what we initially set out to do. Love can lead us into research and love can lead us to be politically active. Love can motivate us to provide the highest standard of medical care possible. Love for our patients also helps us break down the natural barriers that separate us from our patients. If we truly love our patients, we won't neglect the spiritual side of their lives as we treat their physical complaints.

As professionals practicing medicine in a secular world, however, we must approach spiritual issues in an appropriate, non-threat-
ening way. To maintain a professional stance with my patients, I ask
a few questions that can be described as taking a spiritual history.
Along with the family history and social history, I ask about community support and church or mosque or temple attendance. It is then
natural to ask if such religious activities provide them with emotional
or social support. In this way I get a general idea of the role, if any,
that God has in their lives.

Over four years I worked primarily with homeless men and
women, dividing my time between clinics in Washington, D.C. and
Baltimore. Surprisingly, my patients were often much more at ease
talking about spiritual things than I was, and they were often glad
that I, too, am a Christian. Some of the most inspirational one-on-one
Christian fellowships I have known have come from my indigent patients. Perhaps this is precisely because they have nothing and so are
able to see spiritual realities more clearly than I can. They describe
the drama and hardship of their daily lives as a battle between light
and darkness. They themselves often exemplify the power of the
gospel to radically change lives.

After I treated one patient for gonorrhea, I gave him my standard warnings about sexually transmitted diseases. He insisted that
he didn't have anything to worry about because from now on, he
was going to abstain from sexual activity. I was intrigued by his
insistence and carefully obtained a spiritual history. He told me he
had once been an active itinerant preacher in the South. Alone, he
had come to the city to look for work and here he had, in his words,
"fallen into sexual sin." Because he felt guilty, and had lost his self-
respect, he broke off contact with the church. I was the only Christian who knew what he had done. He was remorseful and repentant,
but he had not experienced forgiveness. I suggested that we pray, and
in prayer, I assured him that not only did God forgive him, but also
that God might still want to use him as a preacher. The following day
he was back. He couldn't wait to tell me how happy he was. Leaving
the clinic he had seen a vision of an angel welcoming him back into

fellowship with God.

Alcoholics Anonymous is a natural and professional way to introduce a spiritual dimension into the medical visit. Although A.A. is not necessarily Christian, the Twelve Steps that are the core of the A.A. philosophy were developed directly from the Oxford Group, a Christian movement of the late nineteenth century. "Working the steps" is good for anyone, but is particularly encouraging to watch once-hopeless alcoholics and addicts mature in their Christian faith as they simultaneously recover from their addictions, and grow through A.A.

> **When I make decisions about my work and career, I often ask myself if I am being motivated by fear.**

One way I have encouraged my patients' efforts is by offering them the paperback book, *Serenity: A Companion for Twelve Step Recovery* by Robert Hemfelt and Richard Fowler. This is a New Testament that weaves a discussion of the Twelve Steps into the Gospel texts. When I meet patients on the streets who are carrying tattered, well-read copies of the Bible they received from my office, I can't help but feel optimistic about their recovery.

Perfect love casts out fear

1 John 3:18 reminds us that "perfect love drives out all fear." Fear is often unhelpful, but it is easy to let fear control how we practice medicine. Fear of foreign places and rough neighborhoods can keep health professionals in the suburbs. Fear of impoverished retirement can keep us in high-salaried jobs. Fear of malpractice lawsuits can keep us from starting clinics for the poor. Fear of being unprofessional can keep us from learning how to evangelize, and fear of embarrassment can keep us from sharing Christ with our colleagues and patients. When I make decisions about my work and career, I often ask myself if I am being motivated by fear. Overcoming unhelpful fear has kept my work interesting, but more importantly, it has helped me to trust God. Sometimes God can break through our fear of speaking out, and the result can be humbling and surprising.

Several years ago, a dehydrated, elderly, alcoholic man with end stage liver disease and pancreatitis was vomiting in my examination room. He simply couldn't stop drinking the alcohol that was poisoning his body and his mind. When he stared up at me from the examining table with listless, glassy eyes, I felt helpless. As we waited for the ambulance, I had a minute alone with him. I told him that he was going to die and that alcohol was killing him. Then, uncharacteristically and without permission, I prayed for him aloud, hoping that he would not be offended by my faith.

Six months later, a well-dressed man stopped me on the sidewalk. "I just wanted to shake your hand and say thank you, Doc." I glanced up at a full and smiling face that I didn't recognize. "That prayer you said for me six months ago really made a difference. I haven't touched a drop of liquor since."

Dr. John Umhau, M.D., is a preventive medicine physician in Whiteriver, Arizona. He received his medical degree from Wake Forest School of Medicine and has been in practice for over 30 years. John formerly worked with the homeless in Washington, DC, and Baltimore, as well as working with the National Institute of Health in Washington, DC. He is currently working at Whiteriver Indian Hospital in Whiteriver, Arizona.

CHAPTER 10

SERVING HIM OR THEM

Rosilyn Smith

As a Christian providing healthcare for the poor, I ask myself
almost daily: Why do I continue to work in such a deprived environment? The community mental health center's facilities need major
renovation. With the vacant and boarded-up buildings on our
grounds, visitors often wonder – Am I at the right place?

Is it the salary that encourages me to struggle through the seven
forms needed for each client encounter? Since my salary is about
a third less than that of other board-certified psychiatrists working
in the private sector down the street, surely it's not the money that
keeps me motivated to serve in my present position.

Well then, is it my clients? Now, my clients are great, but they
are unpredictable. I have a fifty percent no-show rate which increases
when the weather is warm and sunny. Most of my patients are here
one week and gone the next. Sometimes they appreciate my expertise
and flexibility, but more often they are indifferent.

Could it be the staff that keeps me here? I really do enjoy working with a dedicated team of mental health professionals who are culturally sensitive to our clients' needs. The staff, however, is frequently overworked, undertrained, and certainly not spiritually attuned to
the real issues of life.

I wonder: What am I doing for those I serve? How does my being here affect the staff of psychiatrists, therapists, and social workers with whom I work? Am I fulfilling God's plan for my life? Am I accomplishing anything for God?

My patients sometimes make it a major challenge for me to appreciate my opportunity to "live out the gospel" among the poor, suffering, and oppressed. When John comes in to see me, for example, I generally grab my can of air freshener and interview him as hastily as possible. Since I have tried to provide care to him over the last three years, I know just what he will say. "No, I haven't been drinking a lot lately. I don't have any money to buy it until the first of the month. Why should I take the medication? I have never needed it. My family committed me to the psychiatric hospital four times for no reason. They lied about me so they could collect my check." Typically John gets upset when I won't agree with him and leaves my office abruptly. Just as the smell of my pine-scented air freshener fades, I realize that the price of serving my patients is more than a $1.59 can of room deodorizer. It is the willingness to encounter with respect the dirty, unlovable, noncompliant, rejected, and sometimes hostile people of our society. I wonder, "Did John smell the aroma of Christ?"

The price of serving my patients is the willingness to encounter with respect the dirty, unlovable, noncompliant, rejected, and sometimes hostile people of our society.

Because I work for a secular organization, I don't pray out loud with my clients. I do pray plenty for myself. Strangely enough, it is not rare for my patients to tell me that they are praying for me – that I will be able to help them through a difficult time in their lives. Many of the people I see are very sick. Frequently they are also tired of the system. For instance, when a woman stomped into my office unannounced and demanded to see a copy of her treatment records, I was caught off guard. My mind began to race. "Who is she? Where is the security guard? Where is her chart?" As I tried to explain the usual protocol for handling medical records, she exploded, "I am not going back to the front window. No, I will not sign in at the front desk. I don't care whether my case is open or closed. I want a copy of my records." I wondered if I could quickly find someone else to handle this request. After all, as the medical director, I should not have to tolerate such an intrusion. But facing reality, I silently prayed for wisdom. I knew that a calm empathetic approach could divert a disastrous outburst. As I began to tease out her concerns, I knew inside that I was going the extra mile, not because it was my job, but rather because my job was my ministry.

Working with non-Christians brings many opportunities to share not only my beliefs but also how these beliefs affect my relationships with them. When I get upset over my secretary's mistakes, I can either "go off" on her and apologize later, or "cool off" and discuss the issue later. Because she is watching me, I am able to maintain a credible witness even in the face of her mistakes.

Am I trying to impress God with my self-sacrificing deep spirituality? Do I have a hidden agenda to bring glory to myself?

The clinic staff at my mental health center is generally warm and empathetic. When therapists and case managers speak to clients with respect, all goes well. Occasionally, however, a staff worker may speak to a client harshly or disrespectfully.

One day, as I passed through our waiting area, I heard Don, one of our staff, talking with a patient that I was referring to the local psychiatric hospital. It was Don's job to make the necessary arrangements. "I have one client ahead of you," he was saying, "Then I plan to eat lunch. I will see you and have you sign the forms after I eat." When I confronted him about his lack of tact, he minimized the matter and pretended to be puzzled by my concern. Now Don and I have an ongoing dialogue about communicating compassionately with clients. Don's heart has not changed, but his behavior has improved.

Am I accomplishing anything for God? It is my own heart that I must check. What is my motivation in serving others, especially those who are poor? Am I trying to impress God with my self-sacrificing deep spirituality? Do I have a hidden agenda to bring glory to myself? Am I genuinely interested in others, or perhaps just polishing my bedside manner? This week the answers are clear to me. I have just returned from a Christian retreat, spending valuable time with the Lord. But, what about next month, when my fingers start to get numb from bureaucratic paperwork? What will be the "word of the Lord" to me?

Dr. Rosilyn Smith, M.D., is a psychiatrist with over thirty years of experience caring for adolescent, adult, and geriatric clients throughout the Greater Philadelphia Region. Dr. Smith received her medical degree from Wake Forest University School of Medicine and completed her training in psychiatry at Hahnemann University Hospital. As an addiction specialist, she treats clients with opiate, alcohol, cocaine, cannabis, nicotine, and PCP dependence. In addition to judiciously prescribing medications, Dr. Smith practices holistic medicine, encouraging wellness in the body, soul, and spirit. Rosilyn is a faith-sensitive psychiatrist, especially competent in cross cultural and interfaith care. She is optimistic that all her clients can enter full recovery. Her husband, Richard, has served as a home missionary pastor for many decades. Together they have developed specialized programs for substance abusers and children.

CHAPTER

11

THROWING DOWN THE ROD

Howard Searle

When I was thirteen years old, I said yes to God's call to serve him through medical missions. Medical missions became my goal through high school and college. It was my reason for entering medical school. It was also my motivation for completing a four-year surgical residency and nine months of anesthesia – skills I would need most in a mission hospital. In medical mission, I saw an opportunity to minister to both body and spirit, and win people for God.

When I completed my training and was appointed by a mission board, people tended to react in one of two ways. Some felt I was crazy – wasting my career. Others put me on a pedestal. The latter response created a phenomenal potential for pride.

When I finally arrived in central India – and this can also happen in underserved areas in the West – I felt somewhat like a big frog in a small pond, so privileged in preparation, yet working in an area with so much poverty and need. Within two weeks of my arrival, I was put in charge of a twenty-five-bed mission hospital. Because I was a missionary – English-speaking and a physician – I was given considerable authority. I didn't mind it at all. I didn't say no to any of it.

Because of my position, local people started asking my advice about important matters – not just medical, but decisions about education, career, and marriage. At first, I felt very inadequate to give advice, and offered it only with humility and hesitation. After a while, I started to volunteer advice. Eventually, I began imposing my advice. It wasn't pretty.

I had succumbed to the temptation to lust for power and control over people's lives and destinies. At the time, if anyone had said that to me, I would have denied it. Perhaps my coworkers would not have seen me as having such a fault. But it was true.

> **I realized that even though I had come to minister through medicine, my attitude did not show Christ's love and concern.**

Then a conflict arose involving a Christian worker from a neighboring area, a colleague, and myself. In time I came to see that in that situation, I was wrong. For the first time, I recognized in myself harshness and a tendency to be authoritarian. I realized that even though I had come to India to minister through medicine, my attitude did not show Christ's love and concern. I asked the Lord's forgiveness for what I was doing, and he enabled me to begin to deal more responsibly with authority and power.

God provided a powerful image to help bring about this transformation when a friend sent me a tape-recorded message by Dr. Martin Lloyd-Jones. He was talking about God's call to Moses and Moses' arguing with God about his call.[1]

"What's that in your hand?" God asked.

"A rod," Moses answered.

"Throw it down," God said.

Now, the Bible doesn't record Moses' arguing with God on that point, but considering how the conversation had been going, I can hardly believe he threw it down without an argument. I can imagine Moses saying, "But God, everything else I had is gone. I'm just a shepherd. This is my security. It's my identity. If I throw it down, there won't be anything of me left."

But eventually, Moses obeyed God and threw it down. And when he did, he saw the rod as God saw it – a poisonous snake that could bite him and perhaps kill him.

Then God said, "Pick it up by the tail."

That is not the right way to pick up a snake. But Moses finally did as God directed, and when he did, it was transformed back into a rod, but with a difference. It was no longer Moses' rod, the symbol of the shepherd, but God's rod, the symbol of the deliverer – with God's power and authority.

When I heard that story, I realized that my rod was my medical and surgical training. I had allowed it to become my sense of identity and security, my place in the world. I also saw that as long as I held it tightly in my grasp, in God's sight, it was really a snake with the power to hurt and destroy me.

God used this insight to help me to throw my rod down and surrender it back to God. When I picked it up again, it was no longer my rod, but God's. I was able to hold it with an open hand, and I have tried to do so ever since.

That experience of throwing down my "rod" before God and picking it up again opened my eyes to see that my work and my God-given medical and surgical skills were not necessarily at the center of God's plan for his ministry through me. There were limits to what could be accomplished through curative care. This awareness opened the door for my transition from a strategy centered on curative care to one including a strong emphasis on community health and development.

It took me ten to fifteen years to realize it, but eventually I came to understand that I could best minister as a member of a team, and not necessarily as the leader of the team. I learned to operate as a part of a community-based healthcare approach that included a physician on the team, but in which the physician played a support role while others with more effective community and people-relating skills took the lead.

I don't believe that I could have come to that place if God had not first remade my self-image. For years, I labored under the burden of a low self-image. I believed that when God made me, he really blew it. He had given me too many liabilities and not enough assets to do the job I felt he had assigned me to do. I revealed this attitude through a highly critical spirit. I would frequently put others down to create positive comparisons with myself: I can do that better than he or she can.

I came to recognize that my attitude was sinful. I was questioning God's sovereignty over creation. I confessed my attitude as sin and acknowledged that God knew what he was doing when he created me. I realized that he had given me everything I needed – real and potential – to do the work he had created and called me to do. That proved very freeing for me. I no longer needed to put others down. Eventually I came to see how God used both my strengths and my limitations to teach me to work as an interdependent member of a team. God had given me my strengths so I would have gifts to offer the team. He had also given me my limitations so that I would know I could minister alone and recognize my need to team up with others with strengths in areas where I was weak.[2]

Healthcare is Christian only to the degree that it expresses the genuine servant spirit of Christ's love.

I learned to collaborate not only with other health and development workers, but with those I was called to serve as well. Early in my ministry, I tended to relate to patients in an authoritative, controlling, answer-providing style where I sought to do things for others. Over the years I learned that I had biases and barriers that often kept me from seeing the real underlying needs of those I was trying to serve. Particularly in community health and development work, I learned to work with people and to ask questions on a group level like:

- What are your needs?
- How would you prioritize those needs?
- What do you see as possible solutions?
- What available resources do we have?
- What additional resources are needed?

Rather than quickly prescribing solutions, I tried to listen to those in need and become a supportive partner with them in their search for solutions.

I believe that this empowering approach to health and development, which was effectively modeled by Christ, can be adapted to the wide variety of medical and health-related opportunities currently available to us. We can ask an individual or group what they see as their needs and help them prioritize those needs. We can discuss possible solutions. What resources can they access without our help? Finally, what additional resources do they need our help in accessing?

As each of us spends time with people, relating to them not as an authority but as a supportive partner, we can build relationships of mutual trust in which they have minimal dependence on us and on the resources we represent. And that trust, gained through empowering interaction, can provide the opportunity for sharing our personal faith in Jesus Christ.

Healthcare is not Christian because it takes place in the context of a Christian institution, or even because the care providers are Christians, motivated by God's call. Healthcare is Christian only to the degree that it expresses the genuine servant spirit of Christ's love.

Howard Searle, M.D., MPH, has served with Emmanaual Hospital Association in India and HEED Bangladesh. Since returning to the United States, he has worked with community health development and child survival programs with MAP International and World Relief. He also works in an urgent care center. He retired 11 years ago and currently serves voluntarily with EHA[USA], a US-based agency, established to encourage prayer and financial support for Emmanuel Hospital Association, an indigenous medical mission serving the marginalized in North India, and operating under Indian missionary leadership – for just over 41 years. Howard and his wife, Becky, make their home in Elgin, IL. They have 5 children and 12 grandchildren.

CHAPTER

12

TO PLEASE GOD

Carolyn Klaus

It should not surprise us when secular and Christian healthcare providers find themselves working toward the same ends. Regardless of their religious orientation, most people's ideas of "what ought to be" bear some resemblance to the kind of healthcare Jesus practiced. Who would not want healthcare to be:

• *Accessible to all, especially the poor?* Jesus performed most of his acts of healing among the poor. "The Spirit of the Lord is upon me," he claimed, "because he has anointed me to bring good news to the poor."[1]

• *Loving?* Jesus taught and modeled the value of caring for "the least of these."[2]

• *Excellent?* It is said of Jesus, "He does all things well!" The work ethic of his followers, even for menial tasks was, "Whatever your task, put yourselves into it, as done for the Lord and not for your masters, since you know that from the Lord you will receive the inheritance as your reward."[3]

• *Focused on prevention?* Jesus spent as much time teaching principles of healthy living as he did healing. He defeated the powers of selfishness and addiction that keep people from doing what they know they ought to do. People who experience his power, which helps them to live according to God's principles, avoiding a great deal of illness.

• *Community-oriented?* Healthy living is not just an individual matter, it's a community affair. From Moses' law onward, God prescribed societal standards that would preserve health and prosperity for his people. The New Testament exhorts the Church to structure itself to help members maintain healthy lifestyles and relationships.

• *Not elitist?* Jesus shared his gifts of healing with his relatively unproven disciples, delegating important responsibilities to them before they had been with him even a year. He spent considerable time training them, rather than always ministering directly to the poor and needy, so that his kingdom would outlast his own life on earth.

But some things Jesus taught are not commonly echoed by the secular prophets. Observance of these truths is what separates Christian healthcare from the best non-Christian healthcare.

> *Healthcare began at God's initiative. God created men and women to be healthy.*

1) Healthcare began at God's initiative. God created men and women to be healthy. When Adam and Eve's sin ushered disease into the world, God immediately began to plan the coming of the one who would reverse that process. Jesus' coming, his healing ministry, and his defeat of the power of sickness and death were all God's idea. Understanding this gives maturation and staying power to Christian providers – something that is beyond mere human compassion.

2) Responsibility for payment for healthcare must be balanced between giver and receiver. Jesus' care was available to all, but sometimes he exacted a high price. He required the woman who was healed by touching his hem to confess before a huge crowd the nature of her illness and what he had done for her.[4] He healed another woman's daughter of demon possession only after she refused to be put off by what could have been taken as a racial slur.[5] He fed four thousand people freely, but only after they had listened to his teaching for three days.[6] On the other hand, no one could accuse Jesus of getting rich from his healings. Jesus warned one would-be follower,

"Foxes have holes, and birds of the air have nests but the Son of Man has nowhere to lay his head."[7] Jesus told his disciples to stay where hospitality was offered them, "eating and drinking whatever they provide, for the laborer deserves to be paid."[8] What would our healthcare system look like if providers agreed to accept only what people were genuinely able to give them, and lived on the same level as those they served?

3) Healthcare must be seen as part of a greater task: preparing the way for the Lord. Jesus' healing ministry was one aspect of his larger mission – to bring the kingdom of God to humanity.

Jesus taught his followers that they were both to preach the kingdom of God and heal the sick. Neither job is complete until the other is done.

Jesus taught his followers that they were both to preach the kingdom of God and heal the sick. Neither job is complete until the other is done. Three years ago, a woman sought care at Esperanza Health Center for acute anxiety attacks and peptic ulcers related to an abusive relationship she endured with her common-law husband. I referred her to one of our counselors who worked several weeks with her and her "spouse," trying to help them relate to each other less painfully. One day I talked to her about God's love for her and his desire to give her new life. To my surprise, she prayed with me and asked Jesus to come into her heart. I referred her to a local church and didn't see much of her after that except to learn that she had finally asked her "spouse" to leave, and her symptoms had resolved. Later on, while I was removing the sutures from her recent appendectomy, she told me she would soon be getting married to a Christian man with a job and a track record of stability. She was beaming. She reminded me that her new life began in our office three years ago. She thanked me over and over for introducing her to the one who changed her life. What if I had only given her tranquilizers? This is not to say that God calls us to lead every patient into a commitment to Christ. Our job, rather, is to probe gently until we see what God is doing in each person's life, and to work with God to help that person take the next step.

4) We are called to tell patients the truth, even when it is not politically correct. Jesus did not simply help people reconnect with their Higher Power or listen to whatever their Inner Guide would tell them. Jesus' ministry was one of separation. He said, "Do you think I came to bring peace to the earth? No, I tell you, but rather division."[9] These words fall harshly on our ears. Even if we see a patient's behavior as wrong, we have been taught that it is unprofessional to challenge it. It is true that we are not to judge or condemn others. But could our reluctance to speak Biblical truth to others come not so much from humility as from fear – fear of rejection by our patients or of disapproval from our colleagues? How would Jesus so sternly confront unrighteous behavior at the same time as he warned people not to judge others? Perhaps true love cannot withhold the diagnosis and prescription for a cure just because it tastes bad. Jesus looked at the rich young ruler, soon to turn away from him, and "loved him." He said, "There is one thing lacking. Sell all that you own and distribute the money to the poor, and you will have treasure in heaven. Then come, follow me."[10] It was a tough prescription, but it would have brought eternal life. Do we care enough to warn patients not just about the medical consequences but also the spiritual consequences of their behavior? Nor can love gloat over, or even be indifferent to, the consequences of the rejection of truth. Jesus wept over Jerusalem, knowing what would happen to it forty years later as a result of its rejection of him. Do we weep over patients who make bad choices for their lives?

5) Christian healthcare is relational. Jesus not only healed and taught people; he associated with them. He went to their parties whether they were religious leaders or tax collectors. He didn't try to keep distance between himself and those he healed, but invited former patients like Mary Magdalene, to join his team of healers. The depth of his involvement with people may have been one of the most powerful components of his ability to heal. In our anxiety to maintain objectivity and prevent burnout, we must not so distance our lives from the lives of our patients that we lose the very relationship that

gives us much of the power to heal.

6) Christian healthcare must be connected to the Church. Health is at least eighty percent nonmedical, involving lifestyle issues, relationships, the person's environment and economics. Physicians can have limited impact on these aspects of health, but the Church is in a position to deal with them directly. Physicians who seek to change the health of their patients need the partnership of the Church.

7) Christian healthcare must be rooted in prayer. Jesus spent hours in prayer, especially at major decision points in his life.[11] The directions he received during those times were not the obvious. Once he was led to leave a town where revival had just broken out, to take the good news to other towns also. Another time, Jesus healed a man on the Sabbath,[12] a serious political faux pas, because he saw his Father at work in the situation. Prayer freed him from the temptation to be dominated by either the visible needs around him or by his own fears. It allowed him to see and respond to God's larger purposes for his life. Only through this type of prayer can healthcare providers remain sensitive to the needs around them, yet not be driven by those needs. Jesus also taught his disciples to look to God to supply all their needs. At Esperanza, God has on many occasions provided staff or finances crucial for the survival of this ministry through highly-improbable channels. This has not only increased the faith of our staff; it has also brought glory to God in the larger community. Healthcare providers who do not feel dependent on God to supply their needs run the danger of slipping into idolatry. But those who do experience God's provision and guidance in answer to prayer can then with credibility encourage patients to trust God to supply their needs as well.

8) Christian healthcare must demonstrate the supernatural. The most obvious evidence of the reign of God in Jesus' ministry was the activity of the supernatural. Praying for the miraculous is neither laziness nor a denial of one's professional training or of the value of scientific advances. While we work as hard as we can and with all the intelligence we possess, we must pray that God will glorify himself above and beyond our limited efforts. At Esperanza, God has

sometimes healed patients in response to prayer in ways that could not be explained medically. We must never take this for granted, but must give thanks for these interventions and continue to pray for them.

9) Servants of God must staff Christian healthcare. In no other area is the difference between Christian and secular healthcare more pronounced. What a person does in private life is usually considered unrelated to what he or she does on the job. The opposite is true in Christian healthcare. Christian health providers are to model what they teach, and encourage others to imitate them.[13] To the provider who lives an unhealthy lifestyle, Jesus declares, "Or how can you say to your brother, 'Let me take the speck out of your eye,' while the log is in your own eye?"[14] The Christian provider's goal must be not just to do good healthcare, but also to please God. And God's highest priority for us is not success in ministry, but holiness – our being set apart for God in every area of our lives.[15] This affects our diet and exercise schedule, our balance between work and rest, and fellowship with God, our relationship with family and friends, and our wallets.

> *God's highest priority for us is not success in ministry, but holiness – our being set apart for God in every area of our lives.*

10) Christian healthcare must respect God as the giver and taker of life. It is not within our authority to participate in active termination of human life, either for unborn fetuses or for persons who no longer value their lives. On the other hand, it is not our responsibility to fight actively against death in every situation when causes we cannot control make imminent death inevitable. We grieve not as those who have no hope.

11) Christian healthcare occasionally confronts the system, representing what God stands for. In the courtyard of the Jerusalem temple, Jesus took a switch and swept out the dishonest moneychangers, even though he knew they would be back the next day. He did so to draw attention to God's purposes. Christian health professionals, too, may be sometimes called on to fulfill prophetic roles in a society that has drifted from God's perspectives on health, responsibility,

compassion, and the value of life. The prophetic role should not be sought, but neither should it be shunned. It is an honor to proclaim and demonstrate God's will. And it is ultimately satisfying, because in the end, God's will indeed be done.

Carolyn Klaus, M.D., is a board-certified internist who became skilled in the care of AIDS patients in a Philadelphia inner city clinic that she founded. Her book, Prescription for Hope, *describes those early days at Esperanza Health Center, which still flourishes twenty years later. With mentoring from an international agency, she also learned to do community development in her neighborhood in Philadelphia. She has used this experience in seven AIDS-affected countries, teaching and consulting in medical schools, colleges and universities, churches, and community-based organizations on four continents.*

In recent years, she has concentrated her efforts in Ethiopia, facilitating the work of 16 denominations to develop a joint AIDS curriculum, training pastors and community leaders on AIDS, and spearheading spiritual and economic development training in several diverse cultural groups. When she is in the USA, she enjoys crocheting, watching American football, and indulging her grandchildren.

TRAINING

CHAPTER 13

MYTHS ABOUT MEDICAL SCHOOL

Mark Mosley

"How can you argue with a man who is firmly convinced that medicine is the best science, that doctors are the best people, and that medical traditions are the best traditions?"
- Anton Chekhov, A Boring Story[1]

Christian students enter medical school with the belief that "God put us here." What we often fail to realize is that the educational system we enter is anti-Christian. We may recognize such obviously anti-Biblical practices as abortion on demand, refusal to treat noninsured (poor) patients, and cutthroat competition for grades. But we may be less alert to the greatest lie of medical school: You must separate your beliefs, especially if they are Christian, from the practice of medicine. Not only do we quietly listen to this lie; we tell it ourselves.

Like many of God's people throughout history, we often unconsciously embrace secular cultural values. If we are to be authentically Christian in our practice of medicine, we must learn to recognize and reject the secular myths that pervade our medical institutions.

Myth 1: Medical schools pick the best people to be doctors.
False. You were picked because you made adequate scores on the
MCAT, had high grades in college science courses, and gave the
overall impression that you thought getting into medical school
would be the greatest thing in the world.

In fact, according to the medical literature, there is little or no
relationship between college grades and professional performance.[2]
Furthermore, MCAT scores have not been good predictors of the
quality of a person's practice. We were picked, then, not because
someone knew we would be good doctors. We were picked because
we fulfilled certain numerical criteria (college grades and MCAT
scores), which now appear to be quite arbitrary.[3,4]

Myth 2: God wants you to make good medical school grades.
A QUALIFIED FALSE. During my first semester in medical school,
a Christian physician told me, "God wants you to make good
grades." I don't think he realized the anxiety he created in me that
day. I was already feeling pressure from friends, parents, relatives,
and myself to make good grades. Now, God was putting the heat
on, too.

While God cares about all aspects of our lives, I dare say that
making "good" grades in medical school isn't even in the top one
hundred. The literature on medical education indicates that there is
almost no correlation between medical school grades and professional performance. The MCAT, NBME, and Flex are recognized to be
inherently flawed because they tend to evaluate test-taking abilities
rather than applied knowledge, analytical thinking, and the commu-
nication of knowledge – skills critically essential in medicine.

While preclinical grades and NBME scores have nothing to do
with being a good doctor, that does not give us a license to be lazy.
As Christian medical students, we should study both medicine and
the Bible diligently, be available to those hurting around us, and pass
medical school. "To jockey for grades, rank, and one-upmanship is in
contradiction to the example and precept of Jesus Christ."[5]

While Scripture directly challenges the competitiveness so

characteristic of medical school,[6] I am ashamed to say that it was the medical literature, not the Bible, which opened my eyes to the foolishness of battling for meaningless grades.

Myth 3: Good residencies require good grades.

False. High-paying specialty residencies require good grades and high test scores. If you want to go into a specialty like ophthalmology, dermatology, or orthopedics, you will need top grades, scores, and letters of recommendation. Why? Because these fields require more knowledge? No. Because they require more diligence? No. In fact, the hours are among the easiest. These specialties are more prestigious partly because they are higher-paying and have relatively easy hours. I am not criticizing these specialties. They are neither better nor worse than others. I am criticizing the way we define "good" residencies.

While good grades, good board scores, and good recommendations may open up more options for residency programs, they do not guarantee that you are more likely to get into a "good" residency – unless you buy into the myth that higher-paying equals "good."

Myth 4: I don't have time for anything but studying.

False. If grades, board scores, and rank have nothing to do with being a good physician, and if "good" residencies can be obtained without finishing top in your class, then why are grades such a sacred cow? Our goals during medical school should include studying both medicine and Scripture diligently, being available to those hurting around us, and passing.

While grades and test scores are meaningless as predictors of who will be good doctors, other criteria are meaningful. Medical data indicate that students are more likely to be "good" doctors (that is, intellectually honest, having genuine concern for patients, of unquestionable integrity, and motivated by service, compassion, and idealism rather than money) if they have volunteer experience, if they take more courses in the humanities and social sciences, if they have premedical and medical school histories of being empathetic, and if they are a source of advice and confidence for their friends.

We could say, then, that medical literature scientifically bears out the good predictors of becoming a "good" doctor which include practicing discipleship, doing volunteer work, lending an ear to others, studying human sciences (ethics, theology, psychiatry, anthropology, literature), while studying hard and passing medical school. Isn't it amazing that even secular medical educators recognize the foolishness of competitive ranking and advocate what are in reality Biblical principles, even without acknowledging God?

Myth 5: Medical information should be value-free.
False. Seven of the ten leading causes of death in the United States are directly related to a person's chosen habits and behaviors, such as smoking, drug abuse, sexually-transmitted diseases, and diet. Habits and behaviors express the values and morals of a culture. To attempt to change behaviors without influencing values, attitudes, and beliefs is futile. Information can change people's knowledge about smoking, alcohol, drugs, sex, or eating, but after decades of research, there is no data to indicate that health information alone, apart from changes in values, results in changed behavior.

Myth 6: The patient always comes first.
False.[7] God always comes first. Sometimes putting God first is expressed through caring for patients and fulfilling your responsibilities as a physician. But sometimes the patient is not even second. If the patient is not critically ill and your work has let up, go home to be with your spouse and children. There are many qualified nurses trained to take care of patients so you can leave the hospital when appropriate. It is baffling how many physicians wander around the hospital till very late hours "just in case something comes up." While they may be among the best-educated and most dedicated physicians, one can't help but wonder if they are equally dedicated to their families.

Myth 7: Medicine is a business.
False. Medicine must be sensitive to money-related issues, but it is by no means a business any more than Christianity is a business. After all, we don't say, "medicine is a legal profession" or "medicine is a governmental agency." Business depends on competition, marketing, advertising, profit, investment, and capital. Good medicine depends on beneficence, service, humility, and patient-centered care not driven by money. The values intrin-sic to medicine are fundamentally different from the premises of law, government, and business. And the same must be said of Christianity. Ed Pelligrino, M.D., has said, "Who would not wither before the gaze of Christ were he to see our fee setting, our bill collecting, our self-justifying unavailability, our put down of the ignorant, our transgression of the values of our patients, our standardizing, mathematicizing, pragmatic assembly-line clinics? We have only to think of his anger with the moneychangers in the temple to remember that hypocrisy was his special enemy."[8]

Myth 8: Medicine is making America healthier
False. Denis Burkitt (of Burkitt's lymphoma) has stated, "Even on a purely scientific level we have probably grossly overestimated the achievements of medical science, yet when one considers man in his true proportions, it is humbling to realize (and more so to acknowledge) how relatively little we have benefited many of our patients."[9]

While no one can deny that we have increased medical knowledge, medical technology, and the amount of our gross national product spent on medical care, it would be a monumental task (if not impossible) to demonstrate that our health is better, whether defined in terms of morbidity, mortality, days taken off work for illness, average life spans, relative dollars spent on an individual's sickness, or lifestyles and behaviors of American people.

Some in the medical profession like to point to increased longevity as an indicator of the profession's success. But when we take a closer look at this average, we find that middle-aged and older people are not living longer. The reason we are "living longer" is because fewer infants and children are dying, raising the average. Is this decrease in child mortality due to medicine? Probably not. "The death rate in children under fifteen had been dropping for almost sixty years before immunizations and antibiotics were available. We like to think that we, as medical professionals, are the ones who have saved the children, but an increase in the standard of living reduced the infant mortality far more than immunizations and antibiotics."[10]

Medical science does an excellent job of treating recognizable disease. It does not, however, address the factors that have the greatest impact on health. Alcohol abuse, for example, is involved of sixty-seven percent of murders, sixty-seven percent of drowning incidents, fifty percent of automobile fatalities, eighty percent of fire-related deaths, thirty-five percent of suicides, and eighty-five percent of deaths from liver disease.[11] Sexually-transmitted diseases are on the increase among adolescents.[12] One out of five Americans has used cocaine.[13] One out of twenty Americans has clinically-defined depressive disorders during a given six-month period.[14] A fourth of the U.S. population is morbidly obese.[15]

In the past two decades, in spite of increased medical information, technology, education, and higher percentages of the GNP spent on medicine, these behaviors have worsened. Is medicine to be blamed? No. Medicine simply has little or no control over such problems as poverty, domestic violence, single-family households, sexually active children, runaway teenagers, overeating, alcohol and drug abuse, and smoking. And since these and other social factors that most affect health are outside the realm of medicine, it would be a mistake to expect the medical profession to be able to do much to make America healthier.

Myth 9: You can't change the system.
False. You can change your own myths about medical school and encourage other believers to do the same. You may be able to change

the opinions of other students and educators using the literature from medical journals that point out the failure of the current system.

I don't believe prayer, Bible study, meeting regularly with other believers, and ministering to the poor are optional for Christian medical students.

To do this, meet daily with another believer for morning prayer or study. Meet often with nonbelievers or nominal Christians for lunch to listen to their needs. Work in an inner-city clinic once a week. You might want to consider moving into a poor community with other Christians to "see healthcare from the streets."

I don't believe prayer, Bible study, meeting regularly with other believers, and ministering to the poor are optional for Christian medical students. These disciplines are the minimum for a "passing" grade in Christian competency. If the medical literature and God's word are correct on this point, these spiritual disciplines may become the most valuable medical learning you will acquire in medical school.

Become knowledgeable about ethical issues. Humanistic students get away with illogical platitudes like, "You should separate your personal beliefs from medicine." Or they reduce the discussion to a personal anecdote: My wife just got an abortion, and she's very well adjusted. Christian students will need to be well-informed in ethics, law, and statistical manipulation if they want to present a Biblical stance.

In your clinical years, don't scrub in on abortions (even if it might mean a lower grade). Consider not scrubbing in on any case with a physician who does abortions.

Avoid saying "the epileptic" or "the diabetic," or even worse, "an epilepsy or diabetes case." Say "the patient with epilepsy," or better yet, "Mrs. Jones, with epilepsy." Make your words and your actions patient-centered and God-centered. Your stance will not be popular, but you will be surprised how respectful people will be if you are knowledgeable, compassionate, and consistent in the way you practice and the stands you take.

Medicine has given us wonderful insights into human behavior and many opportunities to serve others. However, we must not let the good that medicine has done blind us to the myths that have surrounded medicine and become integrated into the value system of the medical education system. If we as Christians do not stand out as different in our thoughts, values, and behaviors in a secular medical school, we must ask ourselves if our Christianity is authentic.

Eighteenth-century British Methodist clergyman Charles Wesley said:

"Why then do not all physicians consider how body disorders are caused or influenced by the mind, and in those cases, which are utterly out of their sphere, call in the assistance of a minister; as ministers, when they find the mind disordered by the body, call in the assistance of a physician? But why are these cases out of their sphere? Because they know not God. It follows, no man can be a thorough physician without being an experienced Christian."[16]

We are not adequately trained for the vocation of healing if we do not devote ourselves to prayer, God's word, medical studies, service to the poor, and listening to those around us in pain. As we prepare to fulfill this "calling," let us take care that our preparation expresses not the values and priorities of an anti-Christian medical education system but the values and priorities of the Great Physician. "For what good will it be for people if they gain the whole medical world yet forfeit their soul?"[17]

Mark Mosley, M.D., M.P.H., is an emergency medicine physician currently serving as the director of quality improvement, the medical director for residency education, and the director of operations management at Wesley Emergency Center in Wichita, KS.

A full-length version of this article appeared in the Journal of Biblical Ethics in Medicine – Volume 3, Number 2. The version that appears herewith was edited by CCHF, for the purposes of this book, and with permission from the author. To see the full-length version, and for a wider list of sources, please visit: http://www.bmei.org/jbem/volume3/num2/mosley_myths_about_medical_school.pdf

CALLED TO SERVE?
DON'T LET HEALTHCARE EDUCATION DEBT STAND IN YOUR WAY

Rick Allen

While attending nursing school, Laura Cooper spent a year doing innercity ministry and eventually volunteered for several months at Christ Community Health Services (CCHS-A) in Augusta, GA.

"God really gave me a vision for CCHS-A and I did not want to work as an RN anywhere else," she said.

One problem loomed: educational debt. Laura's salary at CCHS-A would be much less than she could earn as a nurse elsewhere. Laura and her husband lived frugally – forgoing cable television, buying second-hand clothing, and living in a low-income neighborhood of the city. But both planned to go into ministry and they could not live on their modest income and afford to pay back Laura's educational loans.

More than twenty years ago, MedSend's founders realized that the rising cost of healthcare education, and the associated increase in educational debt, were keeping many healthcare professionals from answering God's call to missionary service. MedSend helped solve this problem by developing funding to repay educational loans for healthcare workers as they minister among the underserved both at home and abroad.

Meanwhile, as medical school costs have continued to rise, medical education debt has mounted as well. The median debt for physicians graduating in 2012 was $170,000, with more than a tenth of private-school graduates owing more than $300,000, according to the Association of American Medical Colleges.[1] The problem is not limited to physicians. Since 1978, college tuition and fees have multiplied over a thousand times. Student loan debt in the U.S. in 2012 was $1.2 trillion, more than the amount of credit card debt.[2]

When God is calling us to healthcare ministry, he will provide all that we need including pathways to provide for educational debt.

"Educational debt has a significant impact on the ability of healthcare professionals who have a vision to serve in underserved settings to do so," says Dr. Timothy Leaman, a site medical director at Esperanza Health Center in Philadelphia. "As the size of educational debt continues to grow, this impact continues to [increase]."

Dr. Leaman points out that that since Christian-based healthcare centers like Esperanza are committed to providing care to many patients who are uninsured or under-insured, and to providing care in a comprehensive model that addresses emotional, social, spiritual and physical health, the cost of care continually exceeds the standard re-imbursement for care.

"One of the ways Esperanza stays solvent despite this gap, is by professional staff working at considerably less than market-rate salaries in order to decrease the cost of providing the services that we believe are so critical to our patients and communities," he says. "But as students are leaving medical training with increasingly large educational debt, the ability to make student loan repayments without outside assistance even with a very frugal lifestyle, at the salaries Esperanza has been able to provide, is virtually impossible." Dr. Leaman speaks from firsthand experience.

"When Jen and I felt God's call to ministry at Esperanza, we knew that the salary they offered at the time was not sufficient to cover my student loans even with our both working at the time and living quite modestly. And that was even with my debt coming out of school being much less than many peers."

A MedSend grant made Dr. Leaman's service possible. MedSend made the monthly payments on Dr. Leaman's educational loans until they were paid off, which enabled his long-term commitment to serving at Esperanza.

"MedSend's grant played an enormous role in God's provision for our family and for Esperanza, and helped facilitate our family being rooted and established in the city for the long term," he says. Esperanza's Director of Community Health and Wellness, Robert Reich, PA-C, MPAS, who also received a MedSend grant that enabled his service, points out that MedSend grants let healthcare professionals become involved with missional healthcare work early in their careers, which is key.

"Some medical professionals may plan to work secularly for a time to pay off debt and then come to a place like Esperanza, but there is a risk that they will become so established in that practice that they never come or it takes them significantly longer to pay off debt than they anticipated," he explains.

Both men believe that a missional lifestyle, including good financial stewardship, is essential for anyone considering healthcare ministry, whether or not they hope to receive a MedSend grant.

"My experience has been that when God is calling us to healthcare ministry, that he will provide all that we need including pathways to provide for educational debt," Dr. Leaman says. "I believe that one of the ways he provides is by giving us wisdom regarding good stewardship of our resources all of the way through our studies and professional life."

As MedSend's President and CEO, I wholeheartedly agree with Dr. Leaman. If you think God has called you to healthcare ministry, I urge you to prepare for future service by living a missional lifestyle now. You will be embarking on one of the most satisfying and challenging careers in the world and you need a time of preparation

– like a boot camp – to develop or reinforce lifestyle disciplines. As a healthcare missionary, those disciplines include daily Bible reading, prayer, fasting, serving others and financial stewardship or money management.

You may not have thought of financial stewardship as a spiritual discipline before, but it is an element of spiritual maturity that affects all aspects of Christian life. As a Christ follower, you should consider all your resources, including your very mind, to be owned by the Lord. He may allow you to possess or use material things, but ultimately all things belong to him.

You should also realize that serving and giving can be hindered by financial debt. Debt of any kind commits you to another. Left unchecked, significant debt can influence or even control your career decisions instead of God. Yet you may be among the many healthcare professionals who must borrow significant amounts of money in order to complete their studies. If so, we want to encourage you to remain as debt-free as possible so you can serve God unencumbered.

Now is the time to learn everything you can about MedSend grants and also about the U.S. Department of Education programs that may provide viable alternatives to MedSend grants. These include the student loan repayment plan called "Income-Based Repayment" (IBR), the student loan forgiveness program, and the HRSA health professions loan repayment, scholarship and loan programs that help to encourage and enable clinicians to work in underserved areas in the U.S.

Before taking any loans, we recommend that you develop and adhere to a financial control plan. Begin with a fairly accurate estimate of how much income you will have available from your student loan account, other income or savings. Then approximate how much it will cost you to live, based on your recent history adjusted to your current situation. Decide how you will disburse your income considering what percentages will go to tithing, taxes, debt repayment, living expenses and necessities, savings and lifestyle.

As you pursue your education, borrow the minimum amount necessary to meet your most basic needs. Before you borrow or accept any type of grant, read all the documents carefully and know what you are agreeing to. If there is a service requirement, be sure you understand what it is and that you feel it is in line with what God is calling you to do. If you do not fulfill the service requirement, it may result in a severe financial penalty, which will make you ineligible for a MedSend grant.

Although some may encourage you to live lavishly, if you believe God has called you to be a healthcare missionary, then you should begin living a missionary lifestyle now. By that we mean:

- Missionaries buy what they need, not what they want. They want what they have. Missionaries can't afford everything they want, but they can afford what they need.
- Missionaries use things up, wear things out, make things do, or do without.
- Missionaries have a conserver mentality rather than a consumer mentality.
- Missionaries don't "shop." They buy with a list of needs and don't buy anything by impulse. Shopping leads to buying things you don't really need.
- Missionaries always maintain the spiritual discipline of giving to God, but not with borrowed money. Sometimes they can only give by self-denial – giving up a necessity in order to give to God.

With regard to borrowing, keep in mind that the less you borrow, the easier it will be for you to enter full-time Christian service and lead a victorious Christian life. Some tips:

- Borrow only for needs, with great care and a budget in hand. Typically, a person with a restrained lifestyle can live on thousands less than lenders recommend.
- To minimize educational borrowing, it often makes sense to attend the least expensive U.S. school you can, which is usually your state university. A conscientious student can get an excellent education in any licensed, reputable program.
- Always think about repayment. Begin making loan payments even before required – as soon as you earn your first dollar – if

at all possible.
- Do not use borrowed money for short-term missions trips.
- If you have educational debt, we recommend limiting tithing to 10% and that you do not support other missionaries. Focus instead on debt-reduction.
- Only use credit cards when absolutely necessary and never for long-term financing.
- Do not make financial investments while in debt, except for employer-paid pensions, IRAs and other tax saving or deferring investments.
- Trust the Lord to provide at every junction along your path.

It won't be easy. You will need great faith and trust to submit to God's direction in managing your material resources. But be assured that when the Lord called you into healthcare ministry, he had already made a way for you to follow him. His great blessings will greatly outweigh the sacrifices you make. Take it from Laura Cooper, who received a MedSend grant that enabled her to continue serving at CCHS-A:

> *"I truly feel that everything in my life thus far has been God's preparation for this work. Now, having been at CCHS-A for 3 years, I can confidently say these have been the most difficult, [yet] most sanctifying years of my life; and that I know Christ [better] for it. Some friends and family still think I am crazy for what I have given my life and education to. However, I am convicted and convinced by God's Word that this is my best answer to the call of the Great Commission. I consider Phil. 3:8 when Paul says, 'I count everything as loss because of the surpassing worth of knowing Christ Jesus my Lord.' It is with that assurance I can also confidently say, this is the life."*

Rick Allen is the president and CEO of MedSend. Rick has a degree in finance and marketing from Temple University. He spent 25 years as a corporate executive, where he was instrumental in the rapid growth and turn-around of several high-tech businesses. In addition, Rick served as Campus Pastor of a multi-site church in Stamford, CT.

15

DON'T MISS THE BANQUET

Rick Donlon

As much as we love Jesus' warm invitations in the gospels ("Come to me, all you who are weary and burdened..."),[1] we have to admit that he spent at least as much time warning us about spiritual dangers. The fourteenth chapter of the Gospel of Luke records one such warning, delivered while Jesus was a carefully watched lunch guest in the home of a Pharisee.

If his hosts were hoping for controversy, Jesus didn't disappoint. He began by healing a man on the Sabbath, an act understood by them to be a violation of the Law of Moses. After that offense, Jesus escalated the tension by exposing the hypocrisy of their Sabbath practices. Next, he reproved his fellow guests for exalting themselves at the expense of others, cautioning them that "...all those who exalt themselves will be humbled, and those who humble themselves will be exalted."[2]

Lastly, Jesus gave instructions about showing kindness to the poor and disenfranchised. When you host a luncheon, he told them, invite the poor, the lame, and the blind. They won't be able to repay the kindness, but a reward will follow at the resurrection of the righteous.[3]

That reference to the final judgment led one of the lunch guests to proclaim, "Blessed is the one who will eat at the feast in the kingdom of God." Interestingly, this statement closely mirrors one made by an angel to the Apostle John near the end of the Book of Revelation, "Write this," the angel said, "Blessed are those who are invited to the wedding supper of the Lamb!"[4]

Jesus used the man's proclamation to tell a cautionary parable describing the factors that disqualify people from participating in the coming Feast or Supper in the fully-realized kingdom of God:

> *Jesus replied: A certain man was preparing a great banquet and invited many guests. At the time of the banquet he sent his servant to tell those who had been invited, 'Come, for everything is now ready.'*
>
> *But they all alike began to make excuses. The first said, 'I have just bought a field, and I must go and see it. Please excuse me.' Another said, 'I have just bought five yoke of oxen, and I'm on my way to try them out. Please excuse me.' Still another said, 'I just got married, so I can't come.'*
>
> *The servant came back and reported this to his master. Then the owner of the house became angry and ordered his servant, 'Go out quickly into the streets and alleys of the town and bring in the poor, the crippled, the blind and the lame.' 'Sir,' the servant said, 'what you ordered has been done, but there is still room.' Then the master told his servant, 'Go out to the roads and country lanes and compel them to come in, so that my house will be full. I tell you, not one of those who were invited will get a taste of my banquet.'[5]*

The parable's final statement must have been jarring for Jesus' original audience and it should be no less alarming to us. Invited guests, known to the master of the banquet, were excluded, replaced by the disenfranchised and the unknown. To put it more concretely, men and women who believe themselves to be on good terms with God will be rejected at the final judgment. Their rejection will occur not because of notorious sins like murder or adultery, but because they preferred the allure of other things, the sort of good things we thank God for. Souls exchanged for a field, a yoke of oxen, or a bride.

Parables teach us profound spiritual truths by making comparisons with familiar objects and processes. Decoding the larger message of this parable is easy enough: the man preparing the great banquet represents God, we are the invitees, and the banquet symbolizes what Jesus called "the resurrection of the righteous" – the judgment and rewards that occur at his final appearing – when evil and rebellion will be removed and he will justly reign forever.

Proceeding further, we need additional spiritual insight to properly understand the meaning of those things that keep the invitees from the banquet. What are we to make of the field, the oxen, and the wife? Drawing from my own experiences and from watching health professional students for the last thirty years, I suggest the following interpretations:

"I have just bought a field, and I must go and see it. Please excuse me."
It's not a coincidence that we refer to our professions as "fields." The term is applied not only to our wider professional categories (nursing, dentistry, pharmacy, medicine, etc.), but also to specialty and subspecialty fields within those disciplines. Our field is the place where we labor, where we harvest a crop of sorts, and where we provide a livelihood for our families and ourselves.

Work in our field is a good thing; it existed before the Fall[6] and, I believe, will exist forever in the eternal kingdom of God. In this present age our work is frustrated by the curse that followed our first parents' rebellion. Nonetheless, our work is a gift from God, and, according to numerous New Testament passages, when we do it, we bring honor to him. How is it, then, that Jesus' parable describes our field as a stumbling block to enjoying the rewards of the kingdom of God?

We don't like to admit it, but most of us who pursue careers in the health professions are proud of ourselves. After all, not just anyone can tackle the academic rigors necessary for success in our fields. We endured afternoon science labs in college while others were playing Frisbee or drinking beer. For years, we pushed through harder courses, bigger tests, and longer hours. We took on debt. We put off relationships and marriage. We delayed gratification.

As we climbed the ladder, we came to understand that all of the health professions have a hierarchy. It's great to be a dentist, but the sharpest graduates go into orthodontics. Being a nurse is noble and patient care is important, but real professionals pursue masters and doctorate degrees. We admit there's a critical primary care deficit in American medicine, but specialties and subspecialties offer better compensation and lifestyles leaving room, we tell ourselves, for generosity, family time, and short-term missions trips.

I've seen students work the God-work equation backwards. They begin with a professional path they want and then retroactively seek God's blessing for it.

Even the most committed disciples, those bent on using their careers in service to Jesus and his kingdom, are susceptible to the insidious influences of professional hubris. We come under the influence of those further along the process, especially professors and mentors. Sooner or later, a respected clinician or academician looks us in the eye and says those magical words, "You know, I think you could be a (fill-in-the-blank) like me someday." The earlier in our training it happens, the more powerful the effect.

There's an insufficiently weighed price for pursuing higher-end training, that extra degree, or a prestigious institution, research opportunity, or competitive specialty. How are we to weigh those costs in light of the kingdom of God?

What if we're genuinely drawn to a high-paying or prestigious career or specialty? Shouldn't there be real-deal disciples of Jesus in every echelon of the health profession? What if we don't feel "called" to be in less rewarding fields? Didn't Augustine say, "Love God and do whatever you please?"

Augustine did say that. And he meant both parts, with the

"whatever you please" part wholly predicated on loving God. Readers of Augustine's Confessions know that he was enthralled with God. He began two of the thirteen chapters with the same quote: "You have broken the chains that bound me; I will sacrifice in your honor."[7] For Augustine, doing whatever one wants isn't an excuse to pursue our own ends; it's encouragement to take the gifts God has given us and lovingly deploy them for his glory.

Too often I've seen students work the God-work equation backwards. They begin with a professional path they want and then retroactively seek God's blessing for it. That's like marrying a stranger and then praying for God to bless the marriage. Things might work out, but it's not an ideal approach.

There's a better, scarier way.

"For I have come down from heaven not to do my will but to do the will of him who sent me." - Jesus, John 6:38

"...because we are convinced that one died for all, and therefore all died. And he died for all, that those who live should no longer live for themselves but for him who died for them and was raised again."

- The Apostle Paul, 2 Corinthians 5:14-15

Our beginning posture is crucial. If we accept the lie that individualistically pursuing our own path will yield happiness and fulfillment, we're at risk of missing the Great Banquet. Everything in our culture and our proud heart tells us that we're the captains of our own ship, limited only by what we can achieve academically and professionally.

The Bible, Jesus, and the Apostles tell us the opposite. We are the undeserving recipients of everything we possess, most importantly our status as forgiven, redeemed children of God. Every advantage we have or ever will have – benefits of family, resources, education, influence, connections, talents, credentials, and any other category of assets – is a temporarily bestowed gift from our King. These gifts are to be deployed on his behalf for his purposes.

Each of us is a miniature Jesus, placed on earth for a short time, not to do our own will, but the will of the one who sent us. We are no longer to live for ourselves, but for Jesus, who died for us and was raised again. In light of these foundational truths, it's inconceivable that we would choose our professional path without his instruction and direction. He's the Master, and we are the servants. Whatever he says, we do. Given his wisdom, his promises, and his love for us, it's foolish to place

Our culture and our proud heart tells us that we're the captains of our own ship, limited only by what we can achieve academically and professionally. The Bible, Jesus, and the Apostles tell us the opposite.

preconditions on our obedience. The money, prestige, and security of a career in medicine are sorry substitutes for the fulfillment and meaning of a life spent for the advancement of God's glory and kingdom.

As we cultivate a habit of subservience and obedience, we learn the reality of Jesus' promise that his sheep hear his voice. Willingly releasing control of our life, including the big decisions surrounding our field, allows us to be led by God into paths we would never have dreamed of, paths of fruitfulness, joy, and, it must be mentioned, suffering. The irreplaceable starting place is surrender to the agenda of God, followed by the application of Biblical principles, and the seeking of confirmation through prayer and godly counsel.

This may seem impractical, given the fact that we're making concrete decisions about our fields. Nothing could be farther from the truth. I've seen students make choices based on far less reliable means, trusting their emotions, yielding to family pressures, or being guided by advice from people who don't fully understand Christian discipleship. Those paths lead to regret.

Submitted, obedient sheep will never miss the call to the Shepherd's banquet.

'I have just bought five yoke of oxen, and I'm on my way to try them out. Please excuse me.'

I've always lived in cities, so I don't know the first thing about farming or cultivating animals. An ox, I had to learn through research, is a castrated adult male cow that is painstakingly trained for the work of plowing, hauling, and treading crops. They often work in tandem with another ox; together two oxen are called a yoke. Some jobs are large enough that they require multiple yokes of oxen. In the pre-industrial age, oxen were the farmer's most powerful and valuable tools of cultivation.

In the Bible, oxen are symbols of both prosperity and strength.

Proverbs 14:4 says, "Where there are no oxen, the manger is empty, but from the strength of an ox come abundant harvests."

In Numbers 24 the prophet-for-hire, Balaam, spoke by the Spirit of God, saying of Israel:

> God brought them out of Egypt;
> they have the strength of a wild ox.
> They devour hostile nations
> and break their bones in pieces.

To quote the Apostle Paul out of context: "Is it about oxen that God is concerned?"[8] No, we've acknowledged that in parables, familiar objects and processes are symbols of deeper spiritual truths. What sorts of things does Jesus have in mind when he warns us not to miss his banquet because we're occupied with teams of cows?

I contend that this is an admonition to avoid the materialism that invariably accompanies work in our "field." Prosperous farmers owned oxen. They were both a means of thriving and a demonstration to others of wealth and strength. Obtaining more oxen, particularly a large number, five yoke or ten oxen, was unmistakable outward proof of one's success.

In medicine, dentistry, nursing and all their related fields, we have corresponding symbols of our success. I remember as a first year medical student longing to put on my new short white lab coat. Before long, I realized that the residents' coats were longer and more desirable. Even more impressive, the attending physicians' coats went nearly to the floor and were freshly starched. Throw in a bow tie and a couple nice pens, and you're due for some serious respect.

For all health professions, there's a predictable arc of success that accompanies our progression. We start out eating mac and cheese in a dorm or a shared apartment. Our car, if we have one, has more than a few miles on it and the "check engine" light may never go out. We likely have borrowed money to sustain us. But all that will change.

Before long, we've got an actual salary. We're able to spend more money and acquire more things. We move from the dorm to a condo or a starter house. We find a nicer neighborhood, one with good schools. As things continue to progress, we have even more discretionary income – or at least access to credit that we can utilize to continue our assent. It's hard to imagine when you're a debt-burdened student, but over the course of a career, most health professionals will see hundreds of thousands of dollars pass through their hands. Physicians and dentists will see millions. Success in the health professions leads to the American Dream on steroids.

Prosperity entices us to see our emerging wealth as the deserved product of our own efforts. We're tempted to fall in line with our profession and the world around us by displaying outward signs of our accomplishments – through what we wear, where we live, what we drive, how we educate our children, our hobbies, where we vacation, etc.

The acquisition and upkeep of these symbols of success require more time and energy than we anticipate. Fashions change, tuitions go up, trips get costlier, and houses need repairs and renovations. Our consumer goods can begin to consume us. Quietly, our hearts and our resources get diverted from God and his kingdom.

Again, this temptation's power is dependent on a widespread but erroneous understanding of our identity. We are not, according to Jesus and the Apostles, self-determining rulers of our own possessions. We are stewards, servants of a Great King who has temporarily entrusted us with his possessions.[9] A steward, according to diction-ary.com, is "a person who manages another's property or financial affairs; one who administers anything as the agent of another."

When we hear about a trustee or guardian who diverted another's

wealth for selfish uses, we call that person an embezzler and a criminal. We send such people to jail. The principle is the same for
Christian disciples. Every material possession we have – not just ten
percent – is God's. He has put these things in our hands for a time,
but there will be a day of reckoning at which time we will give an
account for what we did with his possessions.

The Parable of the Talents makes it clear: those who take the
Master's possessions and use them to get more for the Master receive
great blessing. ("Well done, good and faithful servant… Come and
share your Master's happiness.")[9]

On the other hand, those who fail to see themselves as stewards
and pursue their own interests receive condemnation. ("You wicked
lazy servant… Throw that worthless servant outside, into the darkness, where there will be weeping and gnashing of teeth.")[9]

Every material possession we have – not just ten percent – is God's.

There are strategies that can be
employed, even while one is a student,
to combat the temptation to acquire
too many oxen. The most powerful,
I believe, is to establish a pattern of
generosity that's independent of one's
relative prosperity. Jesus repeatedly told us that if we are faithful
with little, we would be faithful with much. Conversely, if we are not
faithful when we have few possessions, we won't be faithful when
we're successful.

For years, I've asked Christian medical and dental students if
they give away money to advance God's kingdom. The majority do
not, or, if they do, it's sporadic and in small amounts. Their reasoning
often goes as follows: I'm presently a student, reliant on my family
or interest-generating loans to sustain me. For now, I can't afford to
give away money that's not really mine. In the future, however, when
I have an income, I'll begin (or resume) giving money away.

To this Jesus says, "He who is not faithful with little will not
be faithful with much."[9] Remember, for the disciple, it's all God's
money that he has entrusted to us, whether it came from work, our
families, or a loan. We're managing his resources and he has directed

us in the Scriptures to be generous and kingdom-minded. He is fully capable of providing what we need to repay our debts. In my experience, he will do so quicker if we are generous, especially toward the poor and marginalized.

Give now – in a disciplined and regular fashion – regardless of your financial status. If you demonstrate faithfulness in this matter while you are a struggling student, you will be even more generous when God gives you more resources to manage. If you withhold now, for whatever reasons, you will not be a faithful steward later. Remember the one-talent man.

"I just got married, so I can't come."

The greatest earthly blessing I've ever received from God is my wife, Laurie. Nothing else is even remotely close. Marriage is a God-ordained sacramental picture of his love for humanity. Like work, marriage existed before the Fall, although Jesus made it clear that it will not continue in eternity.[10] There are multiple Proverbs that extol the virtues of a good spouse – and many others that describe the suffering attached to a poor marital choice. A spouse who shares your commitment to Jesus and his kingdom will multiply your spiritual impact. "A cord of three strands (husband, wife, and the Lord) is not easily broken."[11] Not all of us will marry, but for those of us who do, marriage can be a great blessing.

Marriage, according to Jesus in Luke 14, can also keep us from the kingdom of God and its rewards.

Over the last twenty-five years I've seen many promising disciples, men and women, who were demonstrating objective evidence of fruitfulness before they succumbed to unwise marital decisions. Their upward trajectory of spiritual maturity flattened and then descended because they gave their hearts to a less committed disciple – or even to an unbeliever. Often, the mismatch was evident before the marriage, but it's exceedingly difficult to convince a young man or woman that they're at risk, once they've given their heart away. The old aphorism, "marry in haste, repent at leisure" is all too true.

We build our spiritual houses one brick at a time. Every small decision has bearing on our ultimate condition; every day incrementally leads us closer to or farther from God. Our choice of mate isn't a small matter, but one of those few truly monumental decisions that profoundly alter our human and eternal courses. Short of the decision to follow Jesus, our choice of mate is probably the most consequential selection we'll ever make.

As in so many medical and spiritual matters, prevention is the best strategy. Christian marriage is covenantal, designed by God to unite two individuals into one flesh. We're not permitted to discard a spouse because we later discover they're not as spiritually compatible as we'd hoped. Before "I do" is the time to wrestle and decide.

I've never known anyone who married someone they didn't first date or, if you prefer, court. Every dating or courting relationship begins with an accepted invitation. Indiscriminate dating significantly increases the risk of an unwise marriage. A related principle: avoiding or disengaging from unhealthy romantic relationships is easiest in the early stages and becomes progressively harder as time and familiarity increase – especially if there is physical intimacy.

> **Every small decision has bearing on our ultimate condition; every day incrementally leads us closer to or farther from God.**

Ten years ago a single young female nurse practitioner moved into our inner-city Memphis community and joined our health ministry. She was a National Health Service Corp scholarship recipient with a three-year loan repayment obligation. She was also completely convinced that God had called her to be a medical missionary. As part of that commitment to missions she'd resolved not to get entangled in romantic relationships with young men who didn't explicitly share her ministry goals. More than one ambitious young man pursued her, only to be politely refused.

One of those young men was a serious and fruitful disciple who had preceded her in the neighborhood by a few years. He was a leader in a sister ministry that evangelized and discipled young men. By any standard, he was a solid Christian and an excellent husband candidate. He was open to the possibility of overseas missionary work, but hadn't felt a clear calling in that direction. She admired him, but declined his invitation to date.

For months he persisted – and so did she. They both prayed for guidance and sought counsel from mentors. Eventually, he became convinced that he was indeed called by God to a very difficult people group in North Africa. They began to date, got engaged, and married. For the last six years they've made disciples, planted churches, and trained other missionaries in a challenging and dangerous part of the world.

My nurse practitioner friend wasn't satisfied with an expressed openness to overseas missionary work; she was looking for a fixed commitment. She furthermore knew that stated commitments should be confirmed by objective evidence. When her suitor began to tangibly move his plans from the Memphis inner city to the Horn of Africa, she knew he wasn't just talking.

I warn my children, especially my daughters, that the best predictor of future behavior is past behavior. If a young suitor says he loves Jesus and is pursuing the life of a disciple, there should be objective evidence of those realities in his life. When I began to date Laurie, I took note that she had been involved in ministry through Young Life for several years, that she was serving as a mentor for younger Christian women, that she loved and knew the Bible, and that she had been on overseas ministry trips. We never fully know a boyfriend or girlfriend until we're actually married, but there are reliable predictors of future behaviors.

Few Christian men or women have the same unwavering resolve as my nurse practitioner friend. Few honestly submit their dating relationships to God or seek guidance from trusted members of the church. Instead, too many fall into disappointing patterns of compromise.

Men know that they're instructed by the Scriptures to seek foremost a wife who reveres and obeys God, but they're too often enticed by the idol of eros. Generally, we're far more likely to compromise on spiritual maturity than we are on physical beauty, rationalizing our disobedience with nonsense about the need for "chemistry." Many young men delay marriage into their mid-thirties or later, in search of a non-existent, sexually-idealized female beauty. Exposure to pornography reinforces those unhealthy and unrealistic expectations. They fear that if they commit to a real woman, one with human imperfections, they'll miss their fantasy wife who's just around the next corner. Delay stunts their own spiritual growth, for marriage confronts us with our selfishness and pushes us, in depen-dence on the Holy Spirit, to love our wives as we love our own bodies. If God blesses us with children, fatherhood accelerates that process of maturity.

Women are nobler, I'm convinced, and I'm far less qualified to render advice to them. Nonetheless, there's a proclivity among some young women to seek financial and physical security for themselves and their future children, rather than abandonment to the kingdom of God.

Much in popular culture reinforces those desires for security. Last night I took my four-year old daughter, Helen, to see the new Disney Cinderella movie. For two hours we watched the courageous and kind Cinderella move toward marriage with the richest and most powerful young man in the realm. Baptizing the temptations of human wealth and power was "true love" – not the erotic, lustful desire that entraps men, but the equally deceptive phantom of eternal romantic attachment. Women are too easily drawn into an idolatrous longing for the perfect wedding, the perfect marriage, and the perfect family. When taken beyond reasonable bounds, desires for a safe and happy home are antithetical to the life of a fruitful disciple.

"I tell you, not one of those who were invited will get a taste of my banquet."
Our marriages and families, like our careers and possessions, must be fully surrendered to Jesus. They are not our own, but temporarily loaned to us for God-centered purposes, namely the glory of God and the expansion of his kingdom. If we don't guard ourselves – from the earliest stages – the temptations of prestige, materialism, and misplaced love will draw us away from our Master and his rewards.

Paradoxically, those who abandon their careers to God's agenda usually experience deeper work satisfaction. Those who pursue generosity are happier, and those who put Jesus above sex and romance enjoy richer marriages.

And these are only the temporary benefits of surrender to the King. He's promised us a Great Banquet with many guests.

Rick Donlon, M.D., is the co-founder of Christ Community Health Services and the founder of Resurrection Health, both in Memphis, TN. Rick has dedicated himself to challenge and inspire students, residents, clinics, and residency programs to express their service to Christ by embracing sustained careers in primary care among the underserved, incarnational living among the poor, and church planting. Rick lives in the Binghampton neighborhood of Memphis with his wife and seven children.

CHAPTER 16

FINDING YOUR PLACE IN THE FIELD

Robert R. Record

By faith Abraham, when called to go to a place he would later receive as his inheritance, obeyed and went, even though he did not know where he was going. By faith he made his home in the promised land like a stranger in a foreign country; he lived in tents, as did Isaac and Jacob, who were heirs with him of the same promise. For he was looking forward to the city with foundations, whose architect and builder is God.

My high school buddies and I jumped at the opportunity for a low-cost co-ed getaway to the desert. Sure the trip was billed as an opportunity to grow as Christians, but we were clearly more invested in our own immaturity than the pursuit of spiritual maturity. I'll never forget the clunker church bus with teen-installed window tinting and a broken air conditioner that trekked us through the summer heat of south Louisiana and across the baked West-Texas landscape. Windows down and shirts off, we howled the anthems of our generation and cracked on one another for a day, a night and a half-day. By the time we reached our New Mexico mountain destination, we had lost weight in our rolling sauna and solidified our commitment to seeking fun at any cost. And we found it. From waking the complex with airhorns to dancing on top of a van to entirely inappropriate music, we were in harmless but rare form that week.

Seeking only my own adolescent entertainment, I somehow found myself in the presence of the eternal during my stay outside of Santa Fe. There, with the testimony of Abraham's descendants so bright in the evening sky, I heard the voice of the Lord. Now, lest you wonder if I was sampling peyote, I've never had any interest in that kind of fun and none of the sound I heard travelled through my vestibulocochlear nerve. But deep in my spirit and more clearly than if I had heard the voice audibly, I knew the Lord had spoken to me, "All or nothing."

Brennan Manning, who even in his passing continues as my favorite author describes moments like these as creating mystics. I honestly don't know much about the theological implications of such a term, but I do know that in that moment with the Almighty, my life transformed from destination to sojourn. Much as Abraham left his people to seek a land God would show him, I left that mountainside with "all or nothing" resounding in my soul knowing I belonged to a King who was both near and beyond me. Those words still echo in my soul 25 years later and have defined my journey both of discovery and action.

"All or nothing" supernaturally integrated into my DNA, I returned home changed, zealous for the study of scripture and the pursuit of Godliness. Although still interested in girls, politics, medicine and sports, I knew there was a calling on my life that trumped even my own affections. On a Sunday evening in rural Louisiana with wide blue eyes, I slowly walked to the front of my protestant congregation to pronounce I was surrendering to the call of ministry. While it was a significant moment, it was seemingly an inevitable step given the call I heard from the Lord on a New Mexico mountain a year earlier.

More Forrest Gump than Bill Gates or Stephen Hawking, I happened upon the discovery of a lifetime. Without agenda, I happened into God's agenda. In responding to "all or nothing", I left all I knew only to find everything was on the other side. This calling led me to medical school rather than seminary in hopes that I would gain a practical skill to serve my neighbors. Along the way, God has partnered me with fellow sojourners. In search of something other than ourselves, we've planted a clinic, a community development work and an inner-city campus of a suburban megachurch. But how did I get here? How did I find a place in the field? More importantly, can I help you find your place? Can I help you respond to God's call on your life?

Fairly frequently, I am asked these questions, usually by sincere students eager to labor for God. Since they are seeking answers only God can give, I instead help them clarify the questions. The first question about the general will of God is always the same, "What is the gospel of Jesus?" I usually get disappointed looks like the one I imagine Elisha must have received from Naaman. After all, they have already embraced the gospel and are in my office for information on what they believe is a different subject. I have them humor me and listen intently to their convoluted though technically correct deliveries of what should be a simple answer.

I respond and have them write this down, "God loves you and has made a way in Jesus for you to receive, return and share that love." That my friends is the gospel, and we cannot go any further in your search for your place in the field until you truly grasp it.

The first word of this gospel definition is intentional, "God". God alone stands supreme. God alone spoke us into being and is worthy of all of our affection and devotion. God alone has every right regardless of how we feel about it to require everything of everyone, including us. To be whole, we must abandon all of our plans and find his, find him. This is non-negotiable.

The second word is equally intentional, "loves". Truly love is the mission of God we are each invited to join, but we cannot join until we allow ourselves to be loved. So I ask my inquirers, do you with all your proclivities and failures honestly believe God loves you? I'm not talking about the counterfeit nonsense that says he loves us but doesn't like us. I mean deep in your soul, do you know that the God of all the universe who has every right to be harsh prefers to like and love you? Do you know his character, and have you found it to be love?

To be honest, most of my eager students have to camp here for a bit to allow the truth to resonate in their own soul. And if they don't get it, I don't go on. To do so would be to run the risk of introducing them to a good calling without them really knowing the God who called them. The outcome of that life may be worse than not pursuing the call at all. I truly see this condition all the time. And it saddens me. People are looking for their place in the kingdom without knowing their place in the heart of the King. Such a fruitless search has a clear biblical name, idolatry. Just for clarity's sake, idolatry is not good.

An article such as this does not afford me the luxury of a week-long pause, so I proceed with a strong word of warning. Tempting as it may be, do not continue to read if you are not convinced of the gospel in your own heart. Enlightenment to the weight of the gospel is discovery of the general will of God and essential to finding anything personal. Design may reveal destiny, but only a loving connection with the designer can truly reveal the design. So be cautioned, the information that follows works. It works so well that it makes life very good even apart from a relationship with Jesus. Pity the person who walks blissfully through life thinking they are doing the will of God only to hear him say as he does in Matthew, "I never knew you, away from me."

Onward! Even after long conversations about the gospel, I well know that I still have in no way satisfied my students' search for the specific will of God for their own lives. Knowing that answers without a journey of discovery usually fail to hold, I ask question #2 about the general will of God. What does God care about? They scratch their heads for a moment as I sit quietly. Over the course of several minutes, my whiteboard inevitably ends up with a list that includes at least the following: his own glory, love, relationship, his kingdom, his church, the lost, the fruit of the spirit, purity, the hurting and oppressed, the poor, widows and orphans and on it goes.

We properly discuss this list pointing out that God is right to care about the spreading of his own glory as it is more than just his fame, it is his character. I briefly mention that perhaps all of us are called to be co-missional with God in the restoring his image in the earth. How do we do that? We live our lives fulfilling the Great Commission by living out the Great Command to love our God and our neighbors.

We then bounce through the scriptures to verify that God is consistent in his desire for everything on the list. Ultimately, we land on the truth that it is the intersection of his values with our life that seeds his rule in our heart. Isn't this the heart of the kingdom? As we meditate on and seek what pleases him, we join the heart of David in Psalm 37 where he beckons, "Delight yourself in the Lord and he will give you the desires of your heart." We are not seeking his to have him bless our wishes, good or bad. Rather, in his presence we find that his very desires become our own. Do you know what those desires are? They are things we listed that he cares about. And at least in part, he has not called you to anything more specific. I have never met anyone consumed with God's desires who is also consumed with where they should live or what profession they should choose.

Allow me to write it plainly. If you will care about what God cares about and design your life around it, you will find great peace and satisfaction and avoid most of life's great problems. This sounds great, right? Well it is, and I have no clue why people can't figure it out or insist on looking for a different way. Simple as it may be, it is truly profound.

However, I've been in my students' shoes, and I am sympathetic to their desires for specifics, so we proceed. Like journalists of old, we are in pursuit of answering the who, what, when, where, why and how of life. I give a nod that we have answered the real who, why and what and that he holds the answer to the where, when and how. Longing for my students to find themselves purely in their "all or nothing" journey of discovery, I share the following story.

Leland and I have four children whom we love dearly. What parents don't, right? It's easier for us because our kids are more awesome than everybody else's. Not bragging, this is just a fact. Our first two are biological and our second two were born into our family by way of adoption from China.

Traveling to get June, our baby, we found ourselves back in Guangzhou. Like every other Westerner, we were taken to the pearl market. Imagine a six story mall with 600 vendors selling nothing but beads that all look alike to the untrained eye. Now that you've done that, you can rest assured that we once again quickly called it quits in favor of an hour at Papa John's. After our pizza and a couple days of recovery, we returned to the market armed with Anne, a Mandarin-speaking personal shopper who was intent on finding us gifts to bring home to family and friends.

With Anne's help we navigated past the visible booths to a hidden part of the building I did not know existed despite two previous visits. How could a *Allow the kingdom to take hold as you actively begin to trade the treasures and systems of this world for something better.* place with so many have even more merchants? She informed us that practically every booth in the building bought their pearls from this single merchant. She went on to pour out his grade B pearls, which were shaped like snowmen, and she explained how this grade was much cheaper. With careful exploration and knowledge from previous transactions, she found enough grade B pearls that were truly grade A and negotiated a deal I could not have imagined. Our success came with searching and sorting. Anne was on a mission not just for any pearls but for the right pearls at the right price.

Even as this encounter played out in a language I didn't understand, my eyes opened to a deeper understanding of Jesus's twin parables in Matthew 13. The kingdom of heaven is like treasure hidden in a field, which a man found and covered up. Then in his joy he goes and sells all that he has and buys that field. Again, the kingdom of heaven is like a merchant in search of fine pearls, who, on finding one pearl of great value, went and sold all that he had and bought it. In that market with Anne, we settled on pearls that were good enough for the simple gifts we intended them to be but not so in life. We must not, we will not settle for trinkets. The kingdom of God is the pearl of ultimate value. And when we have found the rule of God, we acquire it by trading everything we have. The cost of that pearl is great. Its value is greater.

If you are reading this article, it is fair to assume you are intent on living a life that pleases the Lord. You are intent on living life in harmony with divine purpose. I applaud you for your search and hope to help you find a pearl worth all you have.

You've encountered the living God. You know the gospel and are enlightened to both his greatness and his love. You have applied your heart to understanding and have come to embrace God's values rather than the world's. The next step is allow the kingdom to take hold as you actively begin to trade the treasures and systems of this world for something better. Even as Anne helped us navigate the pearl market, I am going to lead you through questions that will require soul searching and answers I cannot give you. I'll give you some thoughts to help guide your meditation, but the real answers must be your own. Beware, the answers to the following questions could lead you anywhere. If you answer these questions properly, you will inevitably be led to life decisions that seem absolutely foolish even to those who know you best. Read and apply yourself at your own risk.

Specific Will of God Question 1: How can I take God's values from aspirational to defining my daily life?
This may seem like what we've already discussed in the more general will of God section. It isn't. You see, it's one thing to say we value something and another thing altogether to allow it to define us. So if you believe God cares about the lost, how is your life organized around helping him find them? If you believe God cares about the church, is your life devoted to a local body of believers? If you believe God longs for you to be pure and to glorify him by reflecting his character through the fruit of the Spirit, are you given to prayer and the study of God's word? If you believe God cares about widows, orphans and the poor, is your life intertwined with any?

If our lives are seeded with the rule of God, these values will inform our daily decisions even when we don't know exactly where we are going. Let's take local church as an example. Given the audience of this publication, I assume many of you are in a professional school, training to have a practical healthcare skill to offer your neighbors. Like many of your fellow students, you've defined your life as too busy for the life of the local church. Please hear this word of correction. You are too busy to not be completely committed with fellow believers. While in medical school, I served as a deacon in my congregation, led a weekly small group with some 30 members and almost never missed a Sunday service all while maintaining very good marks in school. My commitment to God's bride and his system for caring for her gave direction to my present and clarity to my next steps of faith. Church did not rob me of time or focus. On the contrary, it gave me both because I was living in harmony with God's intention. Because I valued what really mattered, everything else fell into its proper place.

I could go on and on with stories that illustrate the importance of living out what we say matters to God. From serving the poor to seeking the lost, the process of allowing our aspirational values to become life-defining is one of being faithful in little things, many very little things. Please pray and ask God to reveal to you where you might be faithful today. Write down what God reveals to you and follow the teaching of Proverbs 3. In all your ways submit to him, and he will make your paths straight.

Specific Will of God Question 2: Do you have a dream, and are you pursuing it with fidelity?
Shortly after my encounter with the Lord in New Mexico, I wrote my personal statement for my college applications. In it I detailed a desire to open an inner-city clinic to serve those in need. Where did that come from? I had never seen an example and knew very little of the inner-city. Yet that dream drove me. It kept me focused and enabled me to say no to many second-best life directions. Through the uncertainty of college and beyond, I was consistently motivated by a clinic that I had never seen.

You have dreams too. Bathed in prayer and covered with wise

counsel, they are right inside you waiting to give direction to your life. The hard thing for many is to know which dream to pursue. I can't answer that, but I can give you a few general rules that will aid your discovery of the big ones. First, God's dream will not violate his revealed will in scripture. Second, pay close attention to dreams that consistently come back even though you try to kill them. Third, be very careful with any dream that might possibly bring you more fame than God. Fourth, if you are having a difficult time dreaming, pour yourself into worship.

As you find the dream, hold on to it. Others can speak into it, but it's not for sale, nor are you. Learn what the dream requires of you. Have a bold willingness to kick in every door that might stand between you and its fulfillment. Match that fire with a bold patience to only walk through the doors God opens. Over time you will see fruit, and you will be able to look back and see how the dream not only drove you but also protected you.

Find the people in your community who are faithfully serving God and bearing fruit. This doesn't make you unoriginal. It shows your wisdom.

Specific Will of God Question 3: What are your gifts and talents?
God did not make a mistake when he made you. From your sense of humor to your intellectual curiosities, you are no accident. Scripture says you are God's workmanship, created in Christ Jesus to do good works, which he prepared in advance for you to do. If he prepared the works, surely he prepared you as well. So go find out what makes you tick. Take personality tests and career surveys to figure out where you might fit best. Ask those who know you best what they could see you doing. I have seen this work well for people more often than not.

As you find yourself, don't be stunned if God calls you to lose some or all of what you have found. The Bible does say that to find our life we must lose it and that we are to die to ourselves. What we have to offer is important but does not define how God chooses to use us as evidenced by so many of the faith giants who have gone before us. Moses, a murderer with a speech impediment, led Israel for years in a way that seemed well outside his gifting. Paul planted churches everywhere and described himself as an unimpressive speaker. Most of the early church leaders died horrific deaths that I doubt would show up as a calling in a spiritual gifts test. There is a great world of work that is beyond our talents. Still, I hesitate to bring up this line of thought with so little space to expand. Why, because it's not proper teaching? No, my problem is with the prevalent false-spirituality teaching in the church that confuses listeners into believing that if you are not miserable you are not really following Jesus. People who teach such are at best mistaken and in desperate need of an encounter with the heart of the Father.

Spend time with the Father. Learn from him how he knit you together. Find out what you are good at and what you enjoy. Perhaps it will end up your vocation or perhaps you'll have to dig ditches to get to do it. When you find it, you'll realize it doesn't really matter if you get paid to do it or not, because you won't be able to imagine life without it.

Specific Will of God Question 4: Where is God working right around you?

It may just be that you are so focused on something so new, distant or special that you haven't really seen what's right in front of you. Find the people in your community who are faithfully serving God and bearing fruit. Get to know them, and see if you can dive into what they are already doing. This doesn't make you unoriginal. It shows your wisdom.

Men and women longing to go to the other side of the world to serve the hurting regularly visit my office for counsel. I love their heart but am often disturbed to learn these same people don't even know their neighbors who live on their block. Don't you think there might be a widow in need, a hungry child or a lost person within minutes of your daily life? Could it be that God has put you right where you are to reach out to that very person? It may not be as romantic as a ten-day journey to a closed country, but it will probably bear more fruit. Jesus' message to pray that God would send laborers into the field applies to all of us. And for most, that field at least for the time being is right next door. Should we ever get the opportunity to serve abroad, learning to love our neighbors here will be the best training available for loving our neighbors there.

Specific Will of God Question 5: Who are you called to serve, and who are you called to serve with?

So many of the searchers I meet are so focused on the when that they don't realize it is almost an irrelevant question. You are in time exactly where you are, and God's kairos will not be thwarted. If you can figure out the people God has given you a supernatural grace to serve and serve with and look for open doors to them, you will find yourself living beyond time. Take the time to learn about different people groups. Spend time in diverse settings making genuine friendships praying that God will give you an unquenchable desire to serve among a specific who.

In my own life, I was drawn to the poor and oppressed at a young age. My mother worked for decades as a social worker at the state mental hospital, and I still remember crying after meeting one of her patients for the first time. We had just finished a Halloween party for employees' children on the grounds and were riding a sugar high in Mom's car headed for the gates when her patient approached the road on my side. I cranked my window down, so we could say hello. His party had been the night before, yet he wondered why he wasn't invited for a second night of fun. It was the actual day after all. My mom patiently explained this party was for children only. He grew angry and flicked his burning cigarette into our car. More heart wrenching than his response was his despair. How could someone hurt so badly over so little and have no hope of anything better? I still wonder.

Beyond Mom's patient, I was fortunate to grow up in the South in the first generation after the Civil Rights Movement. We were increasingly integrated but for many, equal rights were not reality. We found common ground on the ball fields and at the foot of the cross, but a dividing wall still existed in our community. Though I wasn't on the receiving side of inequity, it was still clearly wrong to me. How could a people who believed all were created in the image of God neglect their theology so callously? We believed there was one heaven but lived as if it was divided. Unclear of what response the gospel required of me, I knew it required all of me.

My early years prepared me for a truly integrated and vibrant faith community in a impoverished neighborhood during college in Memphis. It prepared me for CCHF's Steve Noblett's explanation of the kingdom of God in his previous role as pastor of that congregation. In those years I came to know Chet Cantrell in East St. Louis, Illinois on what would become several short-term mission trips. When I saw him fathering the fatherless in a city poorer than I could imagine, something resonated in my spirit. I could imagine no higher calling than the one Chet was living. This revelation of a calling to father the fatherless was tied to a person, and I only could appreciate it because of countless others. We were made for relationship and need others to help us see the road marked out for us. Chet's quiet life has informed every major decision of my life, including calling, vocation, marriage, adoption, ministry and more.

God has created in each of us the need for covenant relationships. Knowing who is in it with us is as important as who we will serve. I believe in this concept so strongly that I tell people all the time, don't do ministry alone. Be willing to, but don't. Jesus went everywhere with the twelve. When he sent out the seventy-two, he did so two by two. Paul always had men serving with him. I've followed the Lord for decades and really can think of nobody who has been successful in ministry doing it alone. I have known several who were convinced they had direction from God to go it alone. Every single one has failed severely. Most have harmed those they felt called to serve and have shipwrecked their own faith. Please don't be the next. Find the people God wants you to serve, and find brothers and sisters of like-heart who will do life in a committed way with you.

Specific Will of God Question 6: Which next step gives God the most glory?
When you feel paralyzed with multiple reasonable paths in front of you, sometimes you just have to take a step of faith. Standing still does not guarantee you will remain in the center of God's will. Perhaps he's actually sovereign and able to work all things for the good of those who love him and are called according to his name. When life is unclear, seek out where God gets the most glory and boldly enjoy your journey.

Nathan Cook shared several years ago at a Christian Community Health Fellowship conference about this very subject. He explained to us Psalm 119:105, Your word is a lamp for my feet, a light on my path. I had always interpreted that verse with a modern day understanding of halogen flashlights. Nathan was better informed, and spoke about how the average ancient oil lamp only gave off enough light to illuminate the next step. Isn't that good? We don't have to know the end to faithfully move forward.

While pursuing what is now Christ Health Center, there were many twists and turns. At one point I was working in an ER as a bridge while we waited for a door to open. The county hospital called and asked if I could help them out as they were in desperate need of physicians. It wasn't my dream job, but it did allow me to take care of the poor. I prayed about it but didn't spend weeks wringing my hands. Not knowing the entire why or where it all would lead, I took the job. God used me in that position and truly used that position to touch me. He now uses the relationships I made there to bless Christ Health Center, our patients and even our city. All of this came from a simple step of faith when I was in limbo and didn't know exactly which way to go. Don't be afraid. Take a step forward.

Final Question: Will you trust Jesus and respond to what he reveals?
Those of us in the medical profession face a confusing travail trenched with obstacles and opportunities that frequently masquerade as one another. From the white coat baptism to the ecclesia of grand

rounds to residency election, we are indoctrinated into a system that has faithfully produced physicians for hundreds of years. Unto its own purpose, the system works fairly well.

We humbly accept the training of the medical system owing much to it. But as much as we are part of that order, our submission is unto a King whose system frequently has countercultural values. Be sure, God has his own purpose. This became quite clear to me in my discussions with the most trusted mentor in my medical school. During third year clerkships, this physician leader pulled me close and said, "Robert, you are too smart for Family Medicine." I was flattered by his encouragement and the fact that he even knew who I was. His opinion carried weight that demanded consideration.

Respecting my accomplished teacher, I prayerfully meditated on his instruction. I considered my aptitude and even my interests in Orthopedics and Ophthalmology. Both were worthy careers, but I could not get past the fact that thousands of communities live without access to even basic care. I was struck with the concept that medicine was not for me a career of self-fulfillment but an opportunity to enter into the sufferings of my neighbors in a transformative way no other profession allows. I fully respect my peers who daily minister to patients in specialty professions, but I could not get past the great need for pastoral primary care physicians. Unlike the fields that most interest me technically and intellectually, if I didn't do Family Medicine, there would one less primary care physician. And so the Spirit used my values and the answers to the questions in this article to make my place in the field clearer.

I'd love to say the path forward from that moment has always been obvious, but I prefer to tell the truth. Ministry opportunities I was convinced were from heaven have evaporated as if their only purpose was to break my heart. Patients we have hoped would find freedom have ridiculed even our best efforts. Neighbors we love continue to suffer and perpetrate violence seemingly without regard for the kingdom's grip on their life. Do we give up? No, no, no, not for a moment. We have found purpose and with it joy knowing we are called and that anywhere other than God's will might as well not exist for us. I long for you to know the strain and paradoxical peace this conviction provides.

The questions are simple, and the answers are readily available to any who are willing. The ultimate question is not to where or even to what you are called, but will you follow in the Way? Oh, that you might find a narrow path impassible in your own strength yet so certain and beautiful you could not imagine yourself on another. Please prayerfully work through these questions aware that the harvest is plentiful. We pray that you find your place in the field.

Question Recap:
1. What is the gospel of Jesus?
2. What does God care about?
3. How can I take God's values from aspirational to defining my daily life?
4. Do you have a dream, and are you pursuing it with fidelity?
5. What are your gifts and talents?
6. Where is God working right around you?
7. Who are you called to serve, and who are you called to serve with?
8. Which next step gives God the most glory?
9. Will you trust Jesus and respond to what he reveals?

Robert Record, M.D., graduated from LSU Medical School and is board-certified in Family Medicine with experience in adult and pediatric primary care as well as emergency medicine. Dr. Record is the founder and CEO of Christ Health Center in Birmingham, AL. He likes to play golf, run, and keep his kids laughing.

17

THE 36-HOUR DAY

Janet Crow

In December 1989, CBS's *60 Minutes* broadcast a feature entitled "The Thirty-Six-Hour Day."[1] The news crew followed medical interns at a teaching hospital through a day, a night on call, and the following day. For most viewers it was doubtlessly another stirring documentary that caused them to shake their heads at the state of the healthcare system in this country.

For me, it was much more. Just six months earlier, with eagerness and anticipation, I had moved to Cleveland with my husband of three weeks to begin my pediatric residency. I was working at a large children's hospital serving a mostly poor, inner-city population. I began my rotations in the outpatient clinic, with call until midnight every fourth night in the emergency room. The thrill of learning new skills and information each day as well as being in the frontline of medicine was invigorating.

My husband and I quickly made friends. Shortly after arriving we found a growing, dynamic church. Greg's job as a mathematics professor didn't start for several weeks, so he soon became the head chef and errand runner. It was great to come home to a hot meal almost every night!

The second month was more difficult than the first. I was on a busy ward of infants with all-night call (where we rarely slept) and continued responsibilities the entire next day, the "thirty-six-hour day." My work week increased to one hundred or one hundred and ten hours, and stayed at that pace for most of the first year. I learned quickly but also began to understand my upper-level colleagues' complaints of constant tiredness. At the end of that month, Greg began teaching, and quick sandwiches or carryout Chinese replaced many of the home-cooked meals.

A few days into my next rotation, one of our fellow interns was seriously injured in an auto accident and had to quit her residency. I was torn between hurting for my friend, who was suffering a major setback, and hurting for myself because I had to scramble along with the rest of the interns to pick up her workload. It was the first of many times we would be asked to add "just one more thing" to an already hectic schedule.

The newness of my internship dulled, and the long, sleepless nights with even longer post-call days were wearing me down physically and emotionally.

As the days got shorter and the sunless autumn of Cleveland set in, my mood began to reflect my surroundings. The newness of my internship dulled, and the long, sleepless nights with even longer post-call days were wearing me down physically and emotionally. The interns complained about everything but never really told each other how they were feeling. I suspect many were experiencing the same exhaustion and hopelessness I was feeling.

By December I was as far from the Christmas spirit as I had ever been. Not only were Greg and I going to spend our first Christmas away from our families, but I was also doing a rotation on an adolescent floor where many of our patients were in terminal stages of cancer. Each new morning was more difficult to face. I lost weight, couldn't eat, cried almost every day, and found myself getting angry and defensive over insignificant things. I had no idea how Greg was adjusting to his new job – I had never asked. My quiet time had dwindled to an occasional desperate cry to God, and even to those cries I seemed to get no response. I felt cold and very alone.

One evening shortly before Christmas I was lying on the couch after a long day at the hospital. Like so many times before, I was longing for my internship to end and wishing I wasn't so tired all the time. Questions flooded my mind. Why was I here? Why had I chosen pediatrics? Why had I become a physician? Why was I still choosing to be alive? The last question scared me. I had never contemplated suicide and was alarmed by the fleeting moment of comfort it brought.

From deep within I began to weep. Tears of bitterness gradually blended into tears of hopelessness and desperation. Greg did his best to comfort me, and we spent time praying together, asking God for comfort and wisdom. Somehow I made it through the every-other-night call schedule of Christmas week, and we flew to Greg's parents' home to spend a few days over the New Year's holiday.

It was the day after we arrived that the "60 Minutes" program aired. I watched, first with interest, then with a growing sense of horror. The past six months were replayed in my mind, and I found myself running to a back bedroom where I buried my head in a pillow to muffle my sobs. I realized then that I had hit my emotional bottom.

That is not the end of the story. I didn't quit. In fact, in just a few months I will be finished and start practicing as a general pediatrician. My situation did not improve overnight. What did happen is that, having come to the end of my self-sufficiency, I began learning to trust God more fully with the details of my life.[2]

I was more fortunate than many residents in that Greg and I were able to quickly find a church and join a small, supportive weekly Bible study group. I attended the group irregularly that year. Though only a few members understood the life of an intern, their constant prayers, along with those of my husband and family, did a lot to sustain me through that time and help me begin the process of healing and rebuilding.[3] I began to find ways to keep myself strong physically, emotionally, and spiritually so I could be effective both at work and at home. Here are a few of the lessons I learned during that time.

Choose a church carefully and prayerfully.

This may seem obvious, but not all churches are alike. It is important to find a group of people committed to Christ, sound Biblical teaching, and meaningful worship. They must also be willing to accept that you may not be there every week, you will occasionally fall asleep during services, you won't be serving as youth director (at least not during residency), and you may not be a good candidate for the board of elders. I'm not advocating a lifetime of minimal involvement in your church; I'm encouraging you to weigh carefully any responsibilities you accept.

Find a person who will hold you accountable in your walk with God.

This may take the form of a Bible study group or a fellow believer at work who will meet with you regularly for Bible study and prayer. You don't have to be going through the same experiences, but you need to be willing to challenge each other at your weak points and encourage each other.

Incorporate God's word into every day.

Notice that I didn't say to start each morning with Bible reading and prayer, though that may be a worthy goal. Quite frankly, there are many mornings when I'm fortunate to roll out of bed, shower, grab breakfast, and make it to work just in time to hear the beginning case of morning rounds. Remember that your relationship with God is dynamic, not static. It requires both commitment and creativity to keep it fresh. Whether you paste Scripture verses to the mirror, memorize passages on call, or pack your Bible in your lunch, including God's Word in your daily routine can be incredibly encouraging during a hectic day.

The same applies to prayer. It has often been while waiting for elevators or accompanying a patient to x-ray that I've finally found a quiet moment to talk to God.

Set aside time to relax.

The person who has most helped me with this lesson is my husband, an avid believer in the Sunday afternoon nap. Though you may not be able to do this every week, you need to have times when you aren't constantly striving to do, do, do, or read, read, read, as is the case for many in the medical profession.

It's also a good idea to develop interests outside your job. Greg and I took up woodworking. Actually, Greg started and I got pulled into it when it came to sanding and staining. We found that we enjoyed working together, and the end products reminded us of those many pleasant hours.

Be assured that God has a purpose for putting you where you are.

God always has something more in mind than just a job, education, or medical residency when he puts us in a particular place. There may be lessons God wants to teach us, or people's lives God wants us to touch.

I will never forget the night that a friend and fellow resident called to say she wanted to tell her mother that she had accepted Christ. After being raised in Pakistan as a granddaughter of a Muslim priest, she had for years been searching for meaning in her life. One day she came to me at work and told me how lonely she was. I invited her to our Bible study and church, and she began to learn about Christ. She finally realized that she could never be good enough in her own strength and that this was why Christ died for her sins. She knew the price of faith would be high for her (perhaps excommunication from her Muslim family), but she got rid of her prayer mat and began to follow Christ.

Medical training is long and often painful. It is also potentially very rewarding. Through the physical and emotional demands they endure, many gain an increased awareness of their patients' suffering and a greater ability to treat them with sensitivity.

I was recently in a friend's office and saw a small piece of paper tacked to the wall by her desk that simply stated:

The will of God
Will not take you
Where the grace of God
Cannot keep you.[4]

How true this has been for me! I pray that God will continue to teach me this in the years ahead.

Janet Crow, M.D., is a pediatrician. She completed her residency in 1992 and is on faculty in the Department of Pediatrics at University of California, San Diego, teaching medical students and residents.

Postscript: In 2003, the Accreditation Counsel for Graduate Medical Education (ACGME) instituted an eighty-hour workweek cap and in 2011 they imposed a sixteen-hour limit per day on work hours for interns. Despite these changes, a NEJM article published in 2012 found that while sixty-two percent of interns thought the new changes were an improvement, nearly half of the senior residents thought their lives were considerably worse. On September 4, 2014, the New York Times published an Op-Ed article entitled "Why Do Doctors Commit Suicide" by Pranay Sinha, a physician in her first year of Internal Medicine at Yale New Haven Hospital. The article was in response to the recent suicides of two medical residents in their second month of residency. She again outlined the immense pressure and fatigue that plagues medical residents despite the changes in work hours. She gives the alarming statistics regarding physician suicide in our country (currently about four hundred per year) and the result of a survey finding that nearly ten percent of fourth-year medical students and interns surveyed reported having suicidal thoughts in the previous two weeks. So while the title of this article is no longer the standard practice of medical residents in this country, the tendency to become overwhelmed and experience incredible hopelessness and fatigue continues, making the observations and suggestions in this article as pertinent today as they were for Dr. Crow back in the early 1990s.[5,6]

CHAPTER 18

EASY COMPROMISES

David Caes

During the eleven-plus years that I worked with CCHF, I had the opportunity to interact with hundreds of Christian healthcare students – most of them medical students. We usually talked about healthcare among the poor, but one thing I noticed again and again was the desire that these students had to use their career in service to God. Those conversations were exciting to me.

But I have noticed that during the long years of medical school and residency something happens to that earnest desire to serve God. The first thing that I noticed is that there are always a lot more students in the beginning of their training who talk about using their career in service to God than there are students who are near the end of their training. Students I interacted with early in their training and who were excited that they could use their service were not that interested in the prospect towards the end of their training.

I poked around and found that there are about twice as many student members of CCHF who are committed to using their career in service to God who are at the beginning of their training as there are at the end of their training. I have noticed the same trends in my visits to medical school campuses and conversations with student groups. This is not the kind of scientific study you read about in medical school texts, but in putting this all together, it seems that somewhere around half of medical students lose their desire to use their career for service to God.

That stunned me, so I started asking around, talking with other people who have been working with healthcare students – people who have been at this business for a while. I found that other organizations had done a lot more research into this, and had a lot better data than I did. One person told me that if only fifty percent of CCHF student members lose their desire to serve God, we are doing extremely well – their organization calculated that the fall-out among student members was closer to eighty to ninety percent!

What happens?

As I have talked with students and those who work with students, I have learned a lot about the pressures on medical students. I have learned about training sites that require Christian healthcare students to live out values that are the antithesis of the Gospel. I have heard about the lack of role models. And then there is the struggle to make good grades. I have learned about the importance of having a small group of people who will hold each other accountable. I have listened to many people talk about the pressure of money, both during and after training. I have learned about the way our vision of service can be worn down by thirty-six-hour days.

Each of these have a strong influence on healthcare students, but I think the most pervasive pressure on students is the choices they make about how to spend their time.

I don't think for a moment that anyone enters healthcare training with the intent of forsaking God by the time that they graduate. But for all too many, that is what actually happens.

I think it starts very subtly. There's a pharmacology exam early tomorrow morning, so it is easy to skip the time you usually spend in prayer in favor of spending it studying. One evening, your time in the pathology text replaces your time in the word of God. On your obstetrics rotation you are up late Saturday night, so you decide to sleep in and skip church. Or you skip the meeting with other Christian students because you really need to do your laundry.

At times, all of us have made these choices. But when you add up the cumulative effect of too many of these compromises, it is all too easy to feel estranged from friends, family, and God. None of those little compromises is going to make that big a difference in your life, but if you add up the cumulative effect of too many of these compromises, you find people not only are feeling a little estranged from God, but have actually forsaken him. I have seen this happen in my own extended family.

You may make decisions about the choices you will make, but the pressure you will experience will mean that you will have to reaffirm those choices every day.

I have heard too many students say that they are very busy in school, and that they had put other things on hold so they could focus on their schooling. When I hear that, I have to wonder if the battle has already been lost.

Is there another way? Is there hope?

I think that there is, but it involves setting standards that are non-negotiable – to decide which things are important to you, more important than even your schooling. You will need to covenant what things you will not give up, even if it means that you have to sacrifice your training. I cannot tell you what those standards are, whether they are deciding how much time you need to spend in prayer or Bible study, or in your church attendance, or even how much time you need to spend with your family and the other people who are important to you. These are decisions that you will need to make. You may make decisions about the choices you will make, but the pressure you will experience will mean that you will probably have to reaffirm those choices every day.

I have a friend who got to the point where she realized that medical school was simply demanding too much. She dropped out, not knowing if she would go back to school. She eventually returned to complete her training, but only after she regained her vision of service to God and was able to reestablish her priorities. I highly respect the difficult choice she made. She is in practice now, and it has been wonderful to see the ways in which God has honored her commitment to him.

The choice is yours. The pressure to compromise these choices will not go away, even after your training years. But through faith, God can grant you the strength to sustain your vision of service to him.

David Caes is the former executive director of Christian Community Health Fellowship. He earned a BA in education from Wheaton College, an M.Ed from National College of Education, and an MBA from Eastern College. David was the editor of Caring for the Least of These, serving Christ among the Poor *and has invested in those seeking to learn more about the theology of serving the poor.*

MODELS OF MINISTRY

19

MISSIONAL COMPONENTS OF A HEALTHCARE MINISTRY

Steve Noblett

Jesus died for people, not organizations. Let's start there. Heaven will be full of people from every language and race, but there won't be any Mercy Health Clinics or Hope Christian Clinics or St. So-and-So Community Health Centers.

Every year I have the privilege of visiting scores of clinics in the CCHF network that serve under-resourced communities. All of them describe themselves as Christian clinics; I always like to ask them, "Why?" Why do they think theirs is a "Christian" clinic? The answers I get are not always simple, one-liners. They have taught me a lot, and have helped me to think more deeply about the various layers or components that healthcare ministries should embrace as they seek to be ambassadors of Christ.

I am a Christian person because Christ died for me. I humbly acknowledged my sinfulness and my need for God. I repented of my sins. I believed that Jesus lives, and that when I turned to him that he would forgive me. I trusted him with my life. (I have never regretted it!) Jesus fulfilled his promise. He did forgive me, and he came into my life. Christ's death and resurrected life were applied to me. That is what makes me or anyone else a Christian person.

But what qualifies a clinic as a "Christian organization"?

It is certainly not the name. If none of the people who work in a clinic know or care about Christ, it doesn't matter whether it has a Biblical name or not. It would be hard to define that clinic as Christian, even if it were well run or had a noble mission. A Christian clinic should be a place where at least some Christians work.

But it is not just the people, either. If an organization were to only hire people who identified themselves as Christians, but everyone on staff were negative, quarrelsome, unhappy, practiced fraudulent billing, offered poor service, and treated people as though they were invisible and unimportant, I doubt any of us would define that as a Christian clinic.

A Christian clinic, at its best, is an organization that aligns its values and mission with God's. It is a place where people who are motivated by the love of Jesus are encouraged to live out their work as worship. It is an organization committed to empowering God's people to do what God has called and gifted them to do, and that works to remove as many barriers as possible so that they may be successful in serving God's purpose. It is a ministry whose leadership and governance recognize and seek to honor the supremacy of Christ by deliberately choosing to run their company in a way that reflects his glory.

This article is not meant to define a standard by which we judge whether a clinic is "Christian enough" to be part of our club. I know organizations that identify themselves as non-faith-based, but allow and encourage Christians to practice excellent medicine while treating patients wholistically and creating a culture that reflects the righteousness, peace and joy that is characteristic of Christ's kingdom. They may not be faith-based organizations, but they are certainly "faith-friendly". These organizations respect the sense of missional calling that their Christian providers and staff feel, and are wise enough to encourage it; and I am happy to identify with them.

Conversely, I have visited clinics that claim to be Christian, but that are rife with inherent strife and a toxic culture created by the staff and leadership. I know of Christian clinics that offer such poor service with such a low standard of excellence that I would not want my granddaughter or my wife to have to depend on them for her care. But if those broken organizations have a desire to honor Christ, then I am committed to invite them as one broken person to another, to turn together to God, lay everything before him, and ask him to forgive, heal and restore us all so that we better represent his kingdom.

The purpose of this article is to challenge and inspire us to fully embrace all that it means to be ambassadors of Christ in a healthcare setting: to develop a culture and pursue a mission in the organizations we create that more faithfully reflect God's mission as it is embodied in the kingdom of God.

The Big Picture

Acts 13:36 says that David served the purpose of God in his generation before he died. That verse has inspired me for many years. It assures me that God has a purpose, and that I am meant to have a part in it. When I began to follow Christ as a college student, I remember being filled with a sense of purpose that I had lacked before. I knew that my life counted for something. Several years later I began to understand more about what God's purpose really is. I am committed to serving his purpose for as long as I have breath.

To be invited to be part of God's purpose is an opportunity to love God in a deeply engaged and meaningful way.

God does not save us because he needs us to complete his purpose. God saves us because he loves us. He enjoys us, and he wants us to enjoy him. But the fact that God has a purpose tells us something about God. His purpose helps us understand what he deems to be important, and what gives him joy. He could keep that purpose a secret, or accomplish it without us. But he has revealed it because he wants us to know his heart, and invites us to participate in his great mission. He created us in his likeness and image, which means that having a purpose fulfills a godly aspect in our nature. Being on mission is part of God's nature, and it is part of our nature, too. To be invited to be part of God's purpose is an opportunity to love God in a deeply engaged and meaningful way. I serve God's purpose, not because he needs me to, but because he allows me to. I want the things God deems as important to be the things I deem as important.

"Many are the plans in a person's heart, but it is the Lord's purpose that prevails."[1] This verse is both a promise and a warning. I am comforted that God's purpose will always prevail. But I am also cautioned that for my ministry to have eternal consequence, then it must reflect God's purpose. If we do not align our mission with God's purpose, then the significance of our greatest efforts will be accidental and marginal at best, and at worst, useless and irrelevant. It is vital that we understand God's purpose, and pour our lives into serving God's purpose in our generation as David did.

God's Purpose Defined

Ephesians 1:8-10 tells us what God's grand purpose is:

"With all wisdom and understanding he made known to us the mystery of his will…to bring into one all things in heaven and on earth under Christ."

Here God states that his plan throughout history has been to unite the spiritual and the material worlds under the headship of Jesus Christ. To say that these worlds are at odds with each other is an understatement. The prevailing global worldview is secularism, a philosophical commitment to life free of spiritual realities. People are largely unaware of what goes on in the spiritual realm; many question whether a spiritual realm even exists. But the physical world does not function well with a broken connection to the spiritual. Because we deny that our actions have spiritual roots and consequences, we have created a culture based solely on what we want. The powerful in economics, academics, military and medicine continually try to brush off, compartmentalize or redefine spiritual accountability, and look at where it has gotten us. In the face of mankind's greatest advances in technology, knowledge and power, we have more wars than at any time in history, slavery is at an all time high, there are more displaced people than ever, disease and depression are out of control, wealth and power disparities are greater than ever, the future looks bleak, and people are generally unhappy.

How we got to this point and what God is doing about it is the story of the Bible. Following God's mission to heal and restore people and their cultures through Christ and his kingdom helps us understand God's grand story.

Following God's mission to heal and restore people and their cultures through Christ and his kingdom helps us understand God's grand story.

In Genesis we read that when God created, he created two realms: the heavens (supernatural or spiritual) and the earth (natural or material). The wording implies that God created these two realms in one massive creative act, and that everything else came out of this initial creation. Each day God gave the command to "let there be…", a word of release, or a command that brought liberty. And each day God judged what he had done by how clearly it represented his intention, "It is good". That is important, because it tells us something about how God governs.[2]

For six days he made light, distinction, dry land, vegetation, a universe full of stars and planets, skies full of birds, seas full of fish, fields full of both wild and domestic animals, and trees and shrubs full of fruit. Everything that he made belonged to either the spiritual realm or the natural realm. By the end of the sixth day, the world was full, beautiful and uncontaminated. Each day the angelic hosts of heaven watched God work in this material realm, bringing order out of chaos; and they sang songs of praise and shouted for joy as he revealed himself in ways that they had never before imagined.

But all of that was simply God setting the stage for his greatest revelation yet. At the end of the 6th day God created a man in his own image. Adam was unique in all of creation. Not only did he resemble God, he was the only thing in God's grand creation that was both spiritual and physical. He was formed of the earth, but made alive by God's spirit. (The Hebrew word for breath is "ruach", which also means spirit.) Man was created as a physio-spiritual being, and in him the two realms were congruent. Mankind was the crown of God's creation, and when God saw what he had made he declared, "it is very good."

God's first recorded words to Adam were a blessing and a commission. God defined man's purpose: to be fruitful, multiply, fill the earth and rule over the physical aspects of God's creation. God gave Adam, this man in his own image and likeness, authority over the natural realm. He was to act as God's representative or ambassador in the earth, and to use his authority to bring fruitfulness, order, maturity and release to God's good and uncontaminated creation.

Adam rebelled against God and set up his own kingdom, one based on knowledge, laws, and systems of justice that were independent of God. The results were catastrophic. As a race, mankind died spiritually, and all that it produced was temporal. Adam subjected all of nature to decay, disruption and disorder. We have hospitals and prisons, wars and violence, brokenness and oppression because one man determined to exercise his authority independently of God's.

In spite of Adam's rebellion, God's plan never changed. When God confronted Adam after the fall, he cursed the devil with a promise that a man would come who would crush the head of the serpent. For the next several thousands of years, and in spite of the attempts of people to replace the one true God with their own creations, God ruled the nations, raising up kings and putting down empires. He sent prophets to remind those in authority that they were accountable to God, and to remind God's people that a king would come who would more than fulfill man's failed mission. It has always remained God's purpose to have a man in his image bring peace and reconciliation through the exercise of godly authority.

In the fullness of time, God sent his son, a "man in his own likeness and image." Hebrews 1:1-3 tells us, *"the Son is the radiance of God's glory and the exact representation of his being."* Jesus was as unique among men as Adam was among the rest of creation. He was born of both God and woman. John the Baptist said that he looked ordinary, and that he would not have recognized him except that the

Spirit of God came on him and remained. He was the only man in history in whom the physical and the spiritual realms were both fully reconciled.

In the person of Jesus, the spiritual and the physical were in absolute harmony. Jesus lived that way. He spoke to men and to demons as though he were at home in both realms, because he was. He had the authority both to forgive sins and to make the lame walk. He was a physio-spiritual being. In him those two realms coexisted.

Jesus lived in perfect submission to his Father. He did not make the same mistakes that Adam made. He never acted independently, though if anyone ever had the right to, it was Jesus. At the beginning of his public ministry Satan tempted him to satisfy his own needs, to defend his own identity, and to take a shortcut to becoming the king of kings, something he knew he was born to do. Jesus passed the test. He remained in perfect submission. Throughout his ministry he said only what the Father wanted him to say. He did the works of the Father, and only those things that he saw the Father doing. Time and time again he was encouraged to bypass the inevitable suffering that he was sent to experience. Each time, Jesus remained submitted to his Father's plan. He held more authority than anyone had ever held. He was more qualified to rule than anyone had ever been. Yet he remained a servant, perfectly submitted, obedient even unto death – and the worst kind of death at that.

Because of his absolute submission to God's plan and will, Jesus has been given the highest of names. After his crucifixion and resurrection, Jesus told his disciples, "All authority in heaven and on earth has been given to me."[3] In light of what we understand God's purpose to be, do you see the significance of that statement? Jesus has been given authority over everything in the realms of the physical and everything in the realms of the spirit. Adam had only ever been given authority over the material realm. But Christ has received all of the authority that Adam lost, and authority over the spiritual realm.

The fact that men live in rebellion to Christ does not diminish the fact that he is their Lord. We do not yet see all things living in submission to him, but we see Jesus, crowned as king/governor/ruler because he remained faithful to exercise his authority under the Father's authority. Christ is ruling now. The expression of his authority may look very different from the way we are used to seeing authority walked out, but make no mistake, Jesus is Lord, and we are all accountable to him.

The good news of the kingdom is that there is a Good King. We have lived in rebellion against him and have broken his laws again and again. But this Good King loves us and is as merciful as he is just. If we simply turn to him in faith and repentance, and recognize him as our Lord, he will forgive us. He has already personally taken the steps to satisfy God's justice on our behalf. When we turn to him, not only will we be forgiven, God will also transform us, baptize us with his Spirit, adopt us into his family, make us co-heirs with Christ who is heir of all things, and include us in his grand work to reconcile all things to himself. But if we reject him, then we remain rebels, and there is no more sacrifice to mediate for us on that day when we must give an account for our independence and rebellion. So turn, bow the knee, and revel in the amazing grace of this Wonderful King.

Called to Advance God's Purpose
It is the mission of God to bring everything under the government of Jesus Christ, and through Christ's kingdom to reintegrate the spiritual and the physical so that they fully reflect the excellence of his nature. In God's wisdom, which I don't pretend to understand, he has chosen to use us to advance that mission. This is our intended purpose. The more we understand about the purpose of God, the more we find his Spirit stirring in us to, like David, "serve the purpose of God in our generation."[4]

Scripture confirms that our mission is to serve God's purpose. When Jesus sent his disciples out it was to proclaim the good news of the kingdom and to demonstrate this kingdom by exercising authority in both the spiritual and physical realms: "Heal the sick, raise the dead, cleanse the lepers, drive out demons. Freely you have received; freely give."[5] Later, when Jesus makes his first mention of the church, he says "I will give you the keys of the kingdom of heaven; whatever you bind on earth will be bound in heaven, and whatever you loose on earth will be loosed in heaven."[6] Never before had authority in both realms been offered to men. Now it has been offered to us through Christ.

Our mission must therefore carry a spiritual component. Earlier I mentioned Matthew 28:18, where Jesus tells the disciples that all authority in both heaven and earth had been given to him. The next verse reads, *"Therefore go and make*

God will accomplish his grand purpose. It is not in question.

disciples of all nations, baptizing them in the name of the Father and of the Son and of the Holy Spirit and teaching them to obey everything I have commanded." Because Jesus has authority over all things, we have a mission that impacts both the natural and the supernatural.

The New Testament writers repeatedly urge us to live on mission. We are encouraged to run the race to win, to not concern ourselves with distracting issues that shift our focus, to recognize that we are vessels made for a holy purpose, to live out every area of our lives with intentionality, to understand that we have been given the ministry of reconciliation (another description of God's purpose to close the gap between the spiritual and the material through a relationship with Jesus), and to be ambassadors of Christ (a title that describes someone who represents the authority of a foreign government).

God will accomplish his grand purpose. It is not in question. There is not a single conditional, or "if/then" statement about Christ's kingdom in the Bible. Christ's kingdom is more than a possibility; it is inevitable. His kingdom is real. It will continue to increase until no challenge remains, and his benevolent authority is recognized and honored over every life, in every nation and institution the world over.

The timing of this grand moment is at least a little bit up to us. 2 Peter 3:12 challenges us to look forward to the day of God and hasten its coming by living godly and holy lives. Most Christians think that holiness refers to sinlessness. But holiness has far more to do with purpose than with the number of sins we commit. The newest, weakest believer is as holy as the most mature saint. That is because

God makes us holy. We are holy because we are set apart for God. We belong to him.

Here is a helpful example. A fork is a fork. But in the Old Testament, there were temple forks that could only be used by priests, and only when they offered sacrifices at the altar. They were not allowed to use ordinary, common forks. Forks used at the altar could be used for nothing else. They were considered "holy". They belonged to God, and had a distinct purpose. In the same way, we belong to God and are reserved to be used as he sees fit. Whenever you read in the Bible that we are called to be holy, you should think, "I have a divine purpose and mission." God's holy people are God's people of purpose. When we serve God's purpose in our generation, we advance his mission and actually hasten the day of his return.

Breaking It Down

We have just looked at the purpose of God from 30,000 feet. You and I are both fruit of his mission and agents of his mission to proclaim and demonstrate the kingdom of God. Organizations we create should reflect our commitment to advance God's mission. We must find ways to communicate spiritual truths in language that the physical world can understand. But we must remain faithful to God's ultimate intention if we are genuinely serving his purpose.

If Christ's kingdom impacts our personal lives, it stands that it also impacts our families, our communities and the institutions that make up our societies. Every Christ-follower is called to represent God's kingdom in our spheres of influence. Education, commerce, criminal justice, military defense, agriculture and healthcare are some of the institutions where we must see the kingdom of God applied in practical ways. You are more than a cog in the massive healthcare machine. You are an ambassador of Christ's government assigned to promote his interests in the medical arena.

Since God's purpose is both material and spiritual, our mission should reflect that. God's purpose involves reconciling individuals and impacting the complex institutions that make up our societies. Our missions should reflect that, too. The missions of our organizations should mirror God's ultimate mission as closely as possible.

What does that look like in healthcare? For those of us who are living out the gospel through healthcare among the poor, what does it mean to align our missions with God's mission? I want to suggest four areas that Christian clinics should develop as part of a Biblical mission. These four components make up a missional focus of organizations that understand their significance as part of a bigger thing that God is doing.

I. Developing a Distinct Christian Culture

Exodus 33 is the story about what happened immediately after Moses came down from Mt. Sinai and found the Israelites worshipping a golden calf. He called on God and interceded for the nation, asking him not to destroy the people. God's initial answer sounded something like, "Okay. I will send an angel ahead of you. He will go to the Promised Land and drive out your enemies so that these people can go in and settle there. But I am not going with you, because my presence carries consequences, and this nation is full of stubborn and stiff-necked rebels."

Moses' reply, paraphrased, was awesome: "Thanks for the generous offer, God. But we would rather fight our own battles than do it without your presence with us. If you won't go with us, we won't go either. *What else distinguishes us from all other peoples on the face of the earth except for your presence!"*

God liked Moses' reply, and went with them. A generation and three million graves in the Sinai desert later, the Israelites crossed the Jordan, fought their own battles, dispossessed people groups who had defiled the land with detestable practices, and settled in a land that had been promised to Abraham 400 years earlier. And they did it with God.

Our first commitment as Christian clinics should be to create an organizational culture that honors the presence of God. People coming to our clinics should be amazed that they encounter God there. You and your co-workers should be constantly mindful that you are doing what you do in Jesus' name, and that he is there in the mix with you. Work should be worship, whether you are the physician, the billing clerk or the CEO.

The fact is when Jesus commissioned us to disciple nations, he promised to be with us always. If we are in Christ, then Christ is in us and with us. Don't ignore him. Nothing would irritate me more than to be in a group of people who talked about me, not to me, as though I were not there. We should treat the Lord with at least the same courtesy with which we treat each other. That may seem like a silly thing to suggest, but when we get busy at work, we forget that God is with us. Honor his presence.

All of us have been in settings where we were aware of God's presence. Usually, it is a sense of peace or joy or love that over-whelms us. Sometimes we feel a burst of faith; or perhaps it is a con-viction of some uncleanness that we have harbored in our lives. I am telling you that you can live that way. God's presence brings peace, power, joy, a sense of holiness. We should guard those qualities by believing that he is with us, and acting like it.

> **Our first commitment as Christian clinics should be to create an organizational culture that honors the presence of God.**

As organizations grow and budgets get larger, it is easy to lose that sense of God's presence. Sometimes we actually downplay the presence of God in order to be more accepting and welcoming of others. But throughout history when God's people honored his pres-ence without apology or hesitation, they grew in number, effective-ness, and respect, and the hearts of those who opposed or threatened them melted.

God's presence does carry consequences. In spite of his presence, the Israelites continued to be unbelieving and stiff-necked. An entire generation died in the wilderness. They died, not because they re-fused to believe God for deliverance, but because they would not be-lieve God for their inheritance.

Several years ago I spoke with the CEO of one of the FQHC's in our network. I asked her, "What has been your biggest challenge as an organization this year?" Her answer took me by surprise:

"Holiness."

I expected it to be billing or EMR implementation, or maybe recruiting. But no. Holiness. She shared how some of the staff (this is a pretty big organization) had become complacent about sin in their personal lives. One person got convicted about it, and shared about a sin issue with her supervisor. The supervisor and the employee then met with the CEO, and they spent several hours on their knees praying for repentance and restoration. The following week the CEO allowed the employee to make an open, public confession, about their sin to the entire staff. Others on staff began to confess their sins, and a revival began to sweep through the entire staff.

I had never heard of anything like that happening in a Christian clinic before, so I asked about it. "That sounds more like church than like a federally funded health center. Help me understand how you think about these things. Why did you include the entire staff?"

The CEO answered, "There is a reason that the Holy Spirit's first name is 'Holy'. If we want the presence of God and for his power to operate through us, then we have to be as serious about holiness as he is."

Leadership like hers should be admired. Building a culture that honors the presence of God requires that we grow as an organization at the rate that we can attract the right kind of team members. It means that we refuse to relate to staff only by how well they perform at their jobs, but that we love one another, recognizing that God put your co-worker there so that both of you can grow in your relationships with Christ. We intentionally look for ways to develop one another in our personal lives as well as our professional lives. It calls us to be intentional and creative in mining God's gifts that he has deposited in your co-workers, always moving to utilize people in their giftedness and not just as position-fillers.

Leaders like the one I described above are more than managers. They embody the values and mission of the organization. A leader that does not overtly value the presence of God in their own life will not bring that value into their organization. Leaders should be symbols for their organization, living brochures that others can examine

to better understand the character of the company they lead.
As you build, look for those kinds of people to lead your organization.

A distinct Christian culture shows dependency on God by making prayer a priority in staff meetings. It is a culture of humility, transparency, and authenticity. It promotes reconciliation among staff, and nips backbiting in the bud. Some organizations do this by having trained spiritual care consultants sit down with staff members that have been unable or unwilling to resolve a conflict. In one situation that I am aware of, the two parties were called into a manager's office to find a cup of grape juice and a small loaf of bread on a table. The manager, with tremendous grace, told them that the goal of the meeting was for all three of them to break bread together at the end of their discussion. Reminded of God's presence, and their call to love and value one another like Christ does, they forgave and affirmed each other in a beautiful moment of reconciliation.

A Christian culture seeks to be an environment where every person feels invested in and important to the mission, allowing for their input and even their mistakes.

A distinctively Christian culture is one of appreciation that pub-lically celebrates achievement and growth in team members. Every 3 months Lawndale Christian Health Center's 500 employees take a break from seeing patients to spend a few hours celebrating their story, worshiping together, and showing public appreciation for co-workers who "got caught" living out the values by which they operate. They call it the Golden Touch Award. Employees nominate one another by sharing the story of a time when the recipient exhibited selflessness, humility and service in a particularly difficult situation. It is the highest honor given: a simple medal, a short story shared of their act read by one of the executives, and shouts, applause and a standing ovation from their peers.

A Christian culture seeks to be an environment where every person feels invested in and important to the mission, allowing for their input and even their well-intentioned mistakes. It is an atmosphere where staff members enjoy one another and enjoy God, and where they perform in roles that are valued and considered significant. Most of all, it never takes the presence of God for granted.

An organization that embraces these practices will be a powerful witness for Christ and his kingdom. John 17:20-23 reminds us that a corporate witness of love, unity and joy amplifies the gospel: "I pray … that they may be brought to complete unity so that the world may know that You sent me and have loved them even as You have loved me."

II. Providing Distinctively Christian Patient Care

There is no question that Jesus prioritized the poor and the marginalized. His inaugural sermon which, outlines his ministry, proclaims that he was anointed by the Spirit of God to bring good news to the poor.[7] He spent his time in rural and blue-collar communities, and went out of his way to be with those whom the religious and privileged avoided.

If Luke 4 was the launch of his ministry, Matthew 25 was the capstone. The last parable that Jesus told and the last recorded act of his public ministry was the story of the sheep and goats. In that parable he describes a scene at the end of the age when the Son of Man as King of the nations will separate all people into two groups. The "sheep" inherit the kingdom, and the "goats" are banished from his presence and given a place in the eternal fire prepared for the devil and his demonic horde.

When one group asks why some get the kingdom while other get eternal fire, the King tells them that their judgment is based on whether they did or did not minister to those who were hungry, thirsty, naked, sick or in prison. But the most amazing part of the story is that Jesus tells them that what they did or did not do to these marginalized people, they did or did not do to Jesus. Jesus identified himself with the weak, the oppressed, the sick, and the needy.

I have heard people refer to this story scores of times in reference to Christians who work in clinics that care for the poor; and they always praise the caregivers for "being the hands and feet of Jesus". But in this parable it is the poor, the prisoner and the sick who are the hands and feet of Jesus. The caregivers are just sheep – really blessed, happy, wealthy sheep.

Matthew 25 helps us understand how we are to treat our patients. We are to care for the patients we serve as though they were Christ himself.

The fact that Christ identifies with this group gives them incredible worth. There is something about our supreme, majestic, sovereign King that can only be revealed through those who are suffering – those who live at the bottom of society. They are image-bearers of God in a unique way that we who live in privilege and comfort are not.

I do not understand this fully; but I cannot deny that I see it in the Scriptures, and I have seen it in my personal experience. I know Christ better for having engaged with people for whom life is a constant struggle. I have found Jesus in the face of the poor.

If Christ were to walk into your clinic with an issue, you would welcome him and treat him in a way that honors his dignity. You would relate to him as a highly trained and capable practitioner, but also as a servant. As medical professionals, it is difficult to treat every patient with that level of dignity, excellence and service; but that is how Jesus treated those who came to him in need, and it is how we should strive – with the help of the Holy Spirit – to treat each of our patients.

Presence is powerful. We have all experienced a health provider who treated us as though we were one twentieth of their daily to-dos. I've been fortunate enough to shadow Christian doctors who are just as pressed and busy as the next guy; but every time they walk into an exam room, they make their next patient feel that they are really there. They breathe warmth, concern, and an eagerness to listen into the exam room, and yet still conduct matters with professionalism and skill.

In Matthew 25 Jesus did not condemn the "goats" for not healing the sick. He condemned them for not visiting and comforting them. Ask yourself, do your patients feel that you were fully present during your encounter? Do they leave their appointment feeling that they have been comforted? This is how Christians should treat patients.

At a conference several years ago I talked about how providers and staff should love their patients. Agape love is a distinct feature of Christian medicine. A surgeon in the audience interrupted, and challenged me. "We don't get that close to our patients! It is inappropriate, and we were intentionally trained to avoid that kind of thing. We cannot love our patients and still deliver the kind of care they need."

Yes, you can. It will mean unlearning some of the style of care that you may have been trained to deliver. It will be painful, and it will take time. And because we are broken and self-centered just like every other Christian, it will

Loving your patient means that you treat them with dignity and recognize that they are people with real stories who are highly valued by God.

require intentionality, discipline and slow progress. Loving your patient does not always mean that you feel deep sentiment for them. But it does mean that you treat them with dignity and recognize that they are people with real stories who are highly valued by God – valued enough that he paid for them with the price of his only son. It means that you treat them holistically, as spiritual people and not just a collection of physical components. Most of all it means that you will seek their good even at the expense of personal sacrifice on your part, regardless of whether they are grateful for your investment in them.

The final two components of being a Christian healthcare ministry are not talked about enough, but are vital if we are to live in the good of all that God has called us to be. It would take too much time to develop them fully in this article, but I hope through this introduction you will explore their implications and embrace them as core values in your ministry: embracing a prophetic role; and replicating and extending our ministries to areas beyond our target communities.

III. Embracing a Prophetic Role

There is a terrific story in Numbers 11 about when Moses cries out to God for help in leading the Israelites through the wilderness. God told Moses to bring 70 elders to the tabernacle, and he would put some of the spirit that was in Moses into the elders. At the appointed time the elders gathered with Moses. God showed up, and took the spirit with which he had anointed Moses and shared it with the elders, and they began to prophesy. Two of the elders, Eldad and Medad, were late for the meeting, but God did not leave them out. While they were still in the streets of the camp the Spirit of God came on them and they began to prophesy, too.

A young man ran up to Moses to tell him that the two elders were prophesying in the camp. Joshua turned to Moses and said, "Tell them to stop!"

But Moses replied, "Are you jealous for my sake? I wish that all the LORD's people were prophets and that the LORD would put his Spirit on all of them!"[8]

Fast-forward twelve hundred years to Jerusalem on the day of the feast of Pentecost. Jesus had recently been crucified and raised from the dead. After spending 40 days teaching his disciples about the kingdom of God, he ascended to heaven leaving his disciples with instructions to wait until they were "clothed with power from on high". For the next 10 days the disciples prayed and waited. When the day of Pentecost arrived, God sent what sounded like a tornado into the room where they were meeting, set their hair on fire, and caused them to stagger out into the temple area speaking in tongues and acting like they were drunk – and the church was born.

What a sight! People in the temple who had come from nations all over the civilized world wondered out loud, "What in heaven's name does all this mean?" Peter stood up to address their questions, and gave his eloquent and provocative sermon, the first post-resurrection gospel call, and a message that has defined the Christian message and mission for over 2000 years.

"This is that about which the prophet Joel spoke when God said, 'In the last days I will pour out my Spirit on all flesh and they will prophesy! Your sons and daughters will prophesy; your young men will see visions and your old men will

*dream dreams. Even on my servants, both men and women,
I will pour out my Spirit in those days and they will
prophesy!"* [9]

The first thing that God had Peter say to help us understand what
the church was about is that we would prophesy. All of us. Men and
women, young and old. Moses' wish was fulfilled. We are meant to
be God's prophetic people throughout this age.

What in heaven's name does this mean?

In the Old Testament, civil authorities, namely kings, governed
the nation. Priests ruled the temple, taught the law, and helped the
people fulfill their worship to God. Prophets were spokesmen for
God who were agents of change when change was needed, and were
great encouragers and builders during key periods of Israel's history.

Prophets are not fortunetellers. God used Prophets to call people
back to his standards. When the people got hyper-religious, but were
not caring for the poor or conducting their business on principles of
righteousness and justice, the prophets called them to account. When
the kings and civil authorities became culturally compromised, the
prophets confronted them. The prophets suffered with the rest of the
people when the nation fell under God's discipline, but reminded the
people of God's mercy and covenant love. When the people were
cocky and prideful, they warned them of imminent demise. But when
they were humbled, enslaved, or in exile, prophets reminded them of
the certainty of God's kingdom.

God has placed us in that role today. In the area of healthcare, we
are responsible to speak for God. We hold the plumb-line of his revealed will up against the broken health systems in our cities and say,
"Hey, this is not what God has in mind. This doesn't look like what
you would expect to find in the kingdom of God. This is broken. By
the way, I am broken, too; and I will show you Who can fix you, me
and this system."

A friend of mine defines being prophetic as "living like tomorrow's people telescoped back into today". We see the features of
God's coming kingdom – righteousness, justice, joy, peace, and compassion. And though we live in a broken and corrupted world, we

choose to live as though that kingdom is here. We do our best to live as a partial fulfillment of Jesus' prayer for God's will to be done on earth as it is in heaven.

Being prophetic requires that we spend time seeking God through his word, through prayer, and examining what he has done in the past. We must learn how to apply the principles of God's kingdom to the institution of healthcare. Prophets do more than just point to what is broken or wrong. They help define and bring clarity. They call broken what is broken, and they point to what should be; and they do it in a way that provokes faith and courage.

> **Being prophetic requires that we spend time seeking God through his word, through prayer, and examining what he has done in the past.**

When I think of people in our movement who fulfill a prophetic role, several come to mind. John Perkins is at the top of the list. Dr. Perkins has used his skills as a preacher to impress on Christians all around the country that justice is an essential part of the gospel. Now in his mid 80s, whenever I hear Dr. Perkins speak I feel emboldened to remain unapologetic and true to the message that there is no real lasting hope apart from the gospel; but that unless the gospel addresses reconciliation and justice for all, then it is not the gospel of the Bible.

Dr. Perkins has helped keep this movement from becoming merely another social initiative. He has used his prophetic role to speak boldly about keeping Christ and the cross at the center of all we do. Dr. Perkins' message has offended a lot of people, mostly those who reduce faith to a private thing that allows them to ignore the plight of the needy and protect their personal comforts. But Dr. Perkins, as a prophet, spends more of his time calling attention to what the church is doing well than he does criticizing her. John helped start CCHF and CCDA (Christian Community Development Association) as organizations to help the church move positively toward responsible engagement with poverty and injustice. I was with John a few weeks ago when he spoke to a wealthy church, and his primary purpose was to encourage them for all of the good and right things they are doing in the community. He is primarily an encourager and strengthener, but is willing to confront injustice when he sees it.

Dr. Janelle Goetcheus is another person in the CCHF community who fully embraces a prophetic role. She and her husband, Allen, moved to Washington, DC to care for the homeless in the late 1970's. For years she trolled dilapidated apartment buildings, parks and bridges to provide medical care for Washington's street people. She worked in emergency rooms to pay the bills, and so that she could get admitting privileges for her homeless patients. In the mid 1980s she built Christ House, an in-patient boarding house for homeless men too sick to be on the street but unable to get into a hospital. To insure that they were "loving their neighbors as themselves", the Goetcheus' and their three children moved into Christ House to live with the homeless men they were serving. Thirty years later, Janelle and Allen still live in Christ House, even though she is the CMO for Unity Health Care, a huge FQHC that sees over a half million patients annually.

Janelle's personal life speaks loudly. But over the years she has been has been a passionate advocate for those who are homeless, uninsured or incarcerated. She publically talked about her difficulties in getting local hospitals to admit her patients or to provide diagnostic tests, which drew a lot of fire from some very powerful administrators. But God used that to open doors that had previously been shut for her patients. She received a large unexpected grant, which enabled her to expand care, and eventually resulted in the formation of Unity Health. Janelle is one of the most soft-spoken, humble people I have ever known, and yet she is a powerful prophetic voice for servant leadership, and for Christ-driven justice and compassion in healthcare.

In smaller but still important ways, Christian health professionals are fulfilling prophetic roles across the country. A physician and a community health worker felt that Medicaid intermediaries and local hospitals in their city had taken a self-interested approach to population health, which excluded many of their neediest patients. So they created a more just and inclusive paradigm of population health that would allow them to provide managed care for both their insured and uninsured patients, and sold the concept to the payers. In places like Buffalo and Nashville pioneer docs saw the rising tide of refugees in their communities. Realizing that they would likely slip through the cracks in healthcare, they designed programs to address the needs of their immigrant neighbors, and have become strong advocates for them to churches and throughout their broader communities.

A big part of fulfilling a prophetic role is simply telling stories. We see the staggering effort that it takes those in poverty to obtain resources that most of us take for granted. We have a unique responsibility to make sure that people understand their struggles. Part of our mission is to make sure that justice and compassion remain on the front burner of the minds of Christians and of those in power. Many will treat justice as just another uncomfortable issue; but for us, it is about people who we know and love, who are created in God's image, who are vulnerable but valuable, and through whom Jesus is revealing himself. The truth is that privileged people need poor people as much as poor people need privileged people.

We know the half-blind, morbidly obese diabetic woman who has to rely on unreliable family members to take her to a doctor's appointment because she lives over half a mile from the nearest bus stop in a neighborhood through which you would not allow your mother to walk. To the ophthalmologist who finally agreed to take one of your patients, she is just another ungrateful no-show. Put on your prophetic shoes, and tell the ophthalmologist that caring for the poor is the right thing to do. Advocate for your patient, and advocate for better understanding between our economically segregated communities.

Prophets are not always popular. We tend to be the folks that make everyone a little uncomfortable. But being prophetic does not always mean being combative. It is okay to get angry at injustice or even at ignorance. But we are called to love both our neighbors and our enemies. Our adversaries are not people, but systems, practices and paradigms that shut out the poor, contribute to disparity, and reward the greedy and the powerful. Like the prophets of old, we identify with God's broken people, and often suffer the consequences for faithfully representing God's interests. That is why the most important aspect of our role is to be a demonstration of our message. Being prophetic means that you are the first to respond to the message God has given you. Being personally invested by sacrificially loving and serving the poor gives weight to our voices as we challenge those in power to do what is right.

> **Being personally invested by sacrificially loving and serving the poor gives weight to our voices as we challenge those in power to do what is right.**

Prophets make easy targets. Another close friend reminded me once that people invite pastors to lunch, but they stone prophets. God never promised us safety or popularity. In fact he promises us persecution, rejection and difficulty. But he also promises us peace, and the comfort of his continual presence. "Blessed are those who are persecuted for righteousness sake…blessed are you when people insult you, persecute you and say all kinds of false things about you. Rejoice and be glad, for great is your reward in heaven, for in the same way they persecuted the prophets who were before you."[10] We are the prophets who have come after the prophets who were before. Let us embrace the prophetic aspect of our mission!

IV. Replicating and Extending Our Ministries Beyond Our Target Community

The healthiest Christian clinics I know are ones that do two things: they engage in genuine, meaningful, responsible mission work outside of their home community; and they train the next generation of medical disciples and leaders.

The needs that threaten to overwhelm our ministries make it seem insane to think about reaching out beyond our target population – but only because we do not see things from God's perspective. God loves our neighborhoods. He is intimately aware of the needs where we minister. But God's heart – his agenda – is worldwide in scope. He is a big God with a big mission. His commitment to cities and nations beyond where you live does not tax his ability or desire to meet the needs in your community. God is thinking about your community, and is just as interested in places far beyond.

That is why, if you are honest, you get excited about seeing God do something great in places far beyond the reach of your target area. The Spirit inside of you longs for the knowledge of the glory of the Lord to fill the earth as the waters cover the sea.

Acts 1:8 gives us the last words of Jesus to the apostles before his ascension:

"You shall receive power when the Holy Spirit comes on you, and you will be my witnesses in Jerusalem, and in all Judea and Samaria, and to the ends of the earth."

Perhaps the most overlooked word in that familiar verse is the word "and". Jesus did not say "Jerusalem, then Judea, then the ends of the earth". Nor did he say "Jerusalem, or Judea, or the ends of the earth". Jesus said "and". While each of us must live out this wonderful commission in the place where we live, we all have a God-planted seed inside us that longs to extend his witness to places beyond us.

CCHF did a survey several years ago of the most effective retention strategies to keep doctors thriving and fruitful in our clinics. We looked at compensation rates, retirement plans, insurance packages, continuing education policies, vacation and PTO. What we found was the most effective retention strategy was for clinics to help pay for providers to do short term medical missions trips to some of the most difficult places on earth. That is right! Doctors and mid-level providers stayed employed longer and reported greater job satisfaction, if after working a year or two in inner-city clinics - where the patients are difficult and have high needs, and where the resources are often very limited - their organization sponsored them to do a two or three week medical mission to north Africa or central Asia where the needs are even greater and the resources are even more scarce. Is that not amazing?

There are several reasons that working beyond your target population is so healthy. It helps give your providers a perspective they would never have if their only focus were your immediate community. It honors their motivating sense of mission and calling. It helps them see their daily work in a greater context of God's greater kingdom work. It stretches them in both their medical skills and in faith in the healthiest of ways. It requires fresh faith from the organizational leadership. (Over time our tendency is to become reliant on well-established systems that no longer stretch our faith. It happens in every ministry. Reaching beyond your resources reengages faith as the modus operendi of your organization.) Most of all, it satisfies something that is uniquely from the Holy Spirit and that stirs in all of us.

Part of your mission should include a strategy to reach out to other strategic places of need beyond your target community.

Dr. Myron Glick and the staff at Jericho Road Community Health Center (JRCHC) in Buffalo, New York, work with a largely refugee population. Over the past decade, God has brought the nations to the doors of their clinic. More than half of their patients are new to America and non-English speakers. JRCHC adopted a strategy to follow their patients back to their homeland, and support them with medical missions. A nurse from Sierra Leone came to Jericho Road as a patient. She became an interpreter; and eventually got her nursing degree, and worked as part of their medical staff. A few years ago she approached Dr. Glick saying that she felt God calling her to go back to her home country and help the people there with Christ-centered healthcare. After several trips, a lot of fund raising, and a well thought out long-term strategy, they built a clinic in the remote area where the nurse had been raised.

They had not counted on Ebola. Their clinic opening coincided with the height of the Ebola crisis in that country. They were able to be a support to other ministries during that time, and miraculously saw no deaths among either their patients or staff. As the crisis is subsiding, many of the temporary medical resources are leaving Sierra Leone, but Jericho Road is staying.

In addition to the work in Sierra Leone, JRCHC is exploring future sites in at least two other West African countries. Having a refugee-focused patient base means that the places they consider as possible clinic sites have been recently decimated by civil war. And though it may seem counterintuitive to multiply when doctors and nurses have been overworked for years, the inclusion and expansion to poverty and war-stricken countries have brought a fresh sense of excitement and faith. Jericho Road is experiencing physical, emotional and spiritual renewal, and is finding new partners and increased resources for its home clinic in Buffalo.

The answer to the mountain of needs we see is not you working longer hours or seeing two more patients a day. The answer is to reproduce yourself.

Part of your mission should include a strategy to reach out to other strategic places of need beyond your target community.

It is also important to have a commitment to train the next generation of Christian medical disciples. Training students means more than using them as volunteers. It means challenging them, and providing them with real clinical education. It should include opportunities for the students to rub shoulders with excellent Christian doctors and leaders who will transparently share about the challenges they face in a career focused on serving the poor. They need to see families that are doing this. They need cultural immersion experiences. And they need us to help them develop a practical theology of mission, justice and suffering that will carry them through the rest of their training.

Every year more than twice as many Christian students want to do rotations in Christian clinics than we have doctors who are willing to precept them. We have enough doctors, but not enough who are willing to train students. That has to change. I often talk to really good Christian doctors who are hesitant to train students. "They slow me down", and "They don't know what they are doing" are typically their complaints.

Remember that you have the skills you have because at some point an older provider put up with you slowing them down and not knowing what you were doing. I realize that working in a non-profit means that we feel the pressure more than others do to hit productivity targets. I realize that most of the clinics in the CCHF family turn away huge numbers of people daily because the needs are greater than our ability to meet them. But the answer to the mountain of needs we see is not you working longer hours or seeing two more patients a day. The answer is to reproduce yourself.

We have an incredible opportunity to disciple our future partners, and to impart the vision and wisdom that God has entrusted to us. The great commission to make disciples should be our first priority. Some of those disciples will go much farther than we have gone. Some will pioneer Christian health ministries in needy communities where there is currently nothing for the poor. Some will lead teams to hard places where poverty and chaos seem insurmountable. But they will go as ambassadors of Christ, committed to demonstrate and proclaim good news to the poor. What a heritage! Impart your life to students who want to integrate faith and medicine.

Organizations that encourage their providers to train students have less trouble recruiting new providers. The two largest Christian clinics in the country employ over 150 full time providers between them. Both organizations recognize the value of training the next generation. They offer summer programs, gap year internships, and they carefully screen medical and PA students who apply for three and four week accredited rotations. Students rotating there are required to lodge in one of the communities where they have clinic sites, in order to provide them a cultural immersion experience. In addition to medical training, students meet with other Christian community development leaders who help them understand how to responsibly address poverty and healthcare injustice. They discuss calling, and the command that Jesus gives us to care for the poor and the marginalized. Students have opportunities to spend time with seasoned providers' families and worship in local community churches.

Over 70% of the students that participate in these programs choose a path of missional medicine and serving the poor as a career. Both organizations have a constant need for new providers, mostly due to growth and to sowing out experienced provider staff to distant medical missions. But these organizations have little trouble finding providers who are eager to work as part of their team. Make replication and extension a core part of your organization's mission, and your organization will always have missionally motivated physicians and providers eager to work with you.

Serve the purpose of God in your generation. Make sure that your organization's mission reflects God's mission to bring all things into compliance with his perfect will under the headship of Christ. Build a culture that honors God's presence. Treat your patients as though they were Jesus, himself. Explore and embrace a prophetic role that advocates for change in our broken communities and institutions. Replicate and extend yourself into areas of need beyond your home community. Live purposefully and hasten the progress of God's advancing kingdom. "Thy kingdom come! Thy will be done on earth as it is in heaven!"

In addition to serving as the Executive Director of CCHF, Steve Noblett serves as an elder at Christ Community Church in Memphis, TN. He and his wife, Victoria, have worked for several decades doing outreach and gospel-driven development in under-resourced urban communities and have been involved in church planting and leadership development.

CHAPTER

20

THE CHOICES:
HOW CAN I BEST SERVE?

Bruce Miller

How can I best serve the medically-underserved? Should I go into private practice and provide my services at a reduced rate or without charge to those who are less able to pay? Should I join a church-operated clinic so that my medical ministry will be integrated into the outreach of a local church or missionary organization? Or would a clinic run by a neighborhood-based board be better, one in which the people themselves are empowered to address their own community's needs? Or might it be better yet – or at least a little more realistic – to join the staff of a secular hospital or clinic, or perhaps a county health department, and minister there? Or could some creative combination of these models be best of all? Most Christian health professionals committed to serving poor people will be faced with at least some of these questions during their careers, some more than once.

Health professionals, church workers, and community organizers who set out to create new structures for delivering health services to the underserved face similar questions: What type of corporate structure should we set up? Should it be church-based or community-based? Should we use a sliding scale for fees? How can we maximize Medicaid reimbursements – or is doing that even ethical? How many billable visits should physicians be expected to generate each day? The list of questions could go on and on.

The Bible doesn't address these questions directly, but it does outline general principles that can guide us when we need to make such decisions. It encourages good, even shrewd, management.[1] Jesus' parable of the talents teaches us that gifts from God are to be invested for the benefit of the kingdom.[2] At the same time, Jesus instructs us not to worry but to share openhandedly with those in need.[3] These passages point us to a balance of management in ministry. We should be wise in business while sharing generously out of trust in God's providence. We are called to a freedom in which we are to serve one another in love.[4] This suggests that various approaches to serving the Lord in health ministry can be appropriate so long as they facilitate loving service.

We should be wise in business while sharing generously out of trust in God's providence. We are called to a freedom in which we are to serve one another in love.

Choosing the best structure for you

The Christian health professional can serve the underserved through any of five kinds of organizational structures: individual private practice, community-based organization, missionary/church organization, secular health organization, and models combining two or more of these structures. Not one model is best for every person or every organization. Each model has its strengths and weaknesses.

Which organizational structure will best enable you or your group to pursue your ministry goals? That depends on several variables. We will analyze each of the five organizational models in light of three of the most important of these variables – personal belief systems, decision-making culture, and financial benefits and limitations.

Personal belief systems. "What would the ideal organization for providing healthcare in a particular community look like?" That is the key question to ask yourself or members of your ministry in order to identify the values that you bring to the organization. Beliefs about an ideal model are potent factors in driving the direction of healthcare ministries.

Some will say the ministry should be governed by the local community. Others will be more concerned about providing care in a setting that simulates private practice, on the grounds that healthcare for the underserved should not take on the atmosphere of a "poor man's clinic." Still others may emphasize the need for an indigenous staff and may see the health center as an opportunity to provide jobs. Just being aware of your own ideas about "ideal structures" and understanding co-workers' beliefs can make it easier for you to work together.

Decision-making culture. The day-to-day working atmosphere in an organization depends a lot on how decisions are made. The decision-making process in many cases grows out of the ideals that governed the design of the organization. For example, if the organization is committed to local community control, the community board may not solicit staff input on many important decisions. A health professional may find it frustrating to have so little voice in how the clinic is run.

Financial benefits and limitations. Each organizational model brings with it financial benefits and limitations, both for the individual and the organization. For the individual, the ability or willingness to live on a higher or lower income makes this an important factor in deciding where to work. Some structures provide more advantages than others for raising operating funds.

Each of these three variables should be weighed when a health professional is considering where to work or when a group that is organizing a health ministry is deciding which model to use.

Model #1: Individual

In the individual model, the Christian doctor goes into private practice and charges his or her patients a fee each time they come in for a visit.

The belief system often driving this approach is that the underserved should be able to receive healthcare in the same kind of setting that others do. It offers hope of avoiding the imposition of an inferior healthcare delivery system on a low-income community. Another value driving the private practice model is that it may be more cost-effective than more bureaucratic models.

The decision-making culture in the individual model is independent and entrepreneurial. Because the practitioner directs the center, the staff is left with few uncertainties about the performance expectations and the direction of the center. One physician had the same receptionist in two settings – first in a community-governed health center, and again several years later in his private practice. The line of authority was much clearer than in the community health center, and she proved far more responsive and cooperative in the private practice.

On the other hand, decisions made by one person rather than a group may not be responsive to the felt needs of the community. The community has no voice in what services are provided and does not experience the benefit of being in a position of empowerment.

The major financial benefit of the individual model is that the same person is responsible for both productivity and finances. The practitioner has strong incentives for carefully managing finances. This is an advantage over other models where the physician is not directly responsible for organizational finances – a fact that can produce constant tension between a physician and administrator. The individual model has financial limitations, however. First, a private practice cannot benefit from the not-for-profit 501(c)3 status that allows foundation support and makes donations tax-deductible. A private practice is usually limited to the provision of reimbursable services. Since services such as health education and counseling are not usually reimbursable, it is unlikely that these will be offered in a private practice.

Second, private practice involves considerable financial risk. It usually requires significant start-up financing and a long-term commitment to develop a regular clientele. For a physician who is called to provide services in a "distant land" for several years, a private practice is not a financially-sound alternative.

Third, the practice must limit the number of low-income clients it can serve. Usually such a practice must be located in a transitional community where at least fifty percent of the patients it attracts are full-paying clients.

Model #2: Missionary/Church

In the missionary model, Christian health professionals leave their own culture and develop clinics (and frequently churches) in cultures different and usually poorer than their own. The ministry is led by individuals from outside the community. In the church model, the health center is a ministry of a local church, and the church leadership is ultimately responsible for the health center.

The belief system behind the missionary or church model includes a conviction that healthcare is inseparable from the church's responsibility to minister to the whole person – body and spirit. Because they operate out of this vision of the church's mission, many Christians see this partnership between church and health center as the theologically required context for healing broken people.

The decision-making culture in this model is shaped by the fact that people who are not a part of the health center's daily operations hold ultimate authority. Whether control is exercised from a distant denominational office or a church down the block, decisions take a long time. On the positive side, the church-operated center has more potential than any other model for tying its patients into a local church.

The financial benefit of tying a center to a denomination or local church is that the revenue base is broadened beyond direct patient revenues. In Mendenhall, Mississippi, and in Pittsburgh, Pennsylvania, for instance, health centers have received subsidies in the form of spaces provided by the local church. Space costs, however, are usually less than fifteen percent of a health center's budget, and few local churches have the funds to provide a significant percentage of a health center's budget.

The financial limitation of being tied to a local church is that the community does not usually feel ownership of the health center. This will limit local charitable contributions. Also, few churches will donate to another church's ministry. Health organizations with roots in the church can be found all across the country, but as the cost of healthcare has escalated, few have maintained those roots. Most have sought broader bases of funding.

Model #3: Community

In the community model, the responsibility for operating and finding money for the local health center rests with local Christians, who then hire health professionals. The organization is governed by a board of directors and normally has a not-for-profit legal structure and 501(c)3 status. The board employs a director to administer the center.

The belief system underlying this model is that local communities are better able to identify and prioritize their needs than professionals who come to the community from the outside. This structure also encourages empowerment of the local community by giving community members the opportunity to make decisions and exercise the responsibilities of leadership and ownership.

The decision-making culture is normally characterized by significant board control. The role and power of the staff versus the board may fluctuate as personalities change. An advantage of this structure is that boards can provide organizational stability during staff changes. The board structure also provides the strength associated with having a number of influential people vested in the organization.

The most common weakness of this structure is the relationship between the board and the staff. The staff members are hired because of their expertise in healthcare, while board members are chosen based on their expertise in facilitating community needs. Both staff and board members usually hold strong opinions on organizational direction. When their views differ, significant tension can develop.

For this model to work, both staff and board leadership must have excellent decision-making skills. These abilities must not be presumed. At the New Hebron Health Center in Mississippi, the breakdown in relationship between board and staff resulted in the center's closing.

The dispersion of decision-making authority may also cause problems in managing staff productivity. Support staff may be less responsive to management when the administration is not the final authority in hiring and termination decisions. A director of a rural health center in Mississippi eventually resigned because he could not effectively manage several unproductive employees who were related board members. Such familiarity between support staff and board members is not uncommon.

The greatest financial benefit of the community-based health center is its IRS tax status, which makes it eligible for government and foundation funding, as well as contributions from individuals. Access to nonpatient-dependent funding allows centers to provide a broader array of health services not common in private practice.

One financial limitation is that community health centers tend to be influenced by a variety of unstated missions. For example, many health centers in low-income communities serve as an important source of employment. This can cause unnecessary increases in staffing and create fiscal inefficiencies. Another weakness is that physicians, who have great influence on whether an organization survives, are not directly responsible for the center's financial well-being. One well-intended physician told me that he was unable to practice quality medicine if he was expected to see more than one patient every half-hour. Not surprisingly, he wanted to work in a salaried position.

On the personal level, one financial limitation is that community-operated Christian health centers often expect their staff to fund a significant portion of the center's cost by accepting salaries less than half of what they could make in a secular environment. It is possible that low wages contribute to high turnover rates.

Model #4: Ambassador

In the ambassador model, an individual Christian works in a secular health organization to meet the needs of the underserved. This model is common but rarely discussed. Opportunities to work in this setting are many: public and private hospitals, state or county health departments, and federally funded clinics are just a few of many possible examples.

This model is not so much driven by a belief system as by one person's calling to impact the existing health system. The choice of this model may also be a practical result of finding no viable alternative. In some communities, working within existing structures may be prudent if new organizations and new people are viewed with suspicion.

The decision-making culture in secular organizations tends to be bureaucratic. Typically, one can expect to have only an indirect influence on policy decisions. If you're easily frustrated by bureaucracy, the ambassador model may not be for you. On the other hand, many Christians find they can invest themselves in the work and be insulated from the worries associated with organizational policy-making.

The financial benefit of participating in a secular organization is entirely a personal one. Though many secular organizations may be as limited as Christian health centers for funding, they do not usually expect staff to work at salaries significantly below market rates. This allows the Christian ambassador more alternatives in lifestyle and more options for financial investment in ministry.

Model #5: Combination

In the combination model, Christians participate in at least two of the models previously described. One example of this is found in Denver, CO, where Bob Williams and Duane Claassen share one position in a suburban private practice and volunteer the other half of their time in an inner-city community health center.

The decision-making culture for this model is largely shaped by the relative financial independence of the Christians who participate. Health worker volunteers are not financially dependent on the health center, which may free the center's leadership to make their own decisions. On the other hand, health workers may want to exercise considerable influence, which can be either good or bad for the organization's mission or finances depending on the particular situation and personalities involved.

The financial benefit is obvious when staff provides services on a volunteer basis, but there are also financial limitations associated with this arrangement. For the volunteer, it is the cost of lost wages. For the health center, it is the cost of losing the leverage that comes from paying someone's salary. Volunteers tend to define the services they wish to provide. A volunteer CPA may not be as punctual as one who is paid.

A volunteer physician may not wish to see as many patients as the health center might like. I know of one health center where a volunteer physician sees about one patient per hour. Though the physician services are donated, the center must still pay support staff and building costs at near market rate. In this case, it's not clear that a free physician's services certainly benefit the organization's mission.

Each of these five organizational models has advantages and disadvantages. Carefully considering the strengths and weaknesses of each in relation to your belief system, your preference for a particular decision-making culture, and your financial goals and needs can help you determine which model can best free you and your organization to serve others in love.

Bruce Miller is the CEO of Lawndale Christian Health Center (LCHC) where he has been employed since 1998. LCHC is a faith-driven, federally-qualified health center focused on improving the health of low-income communities on Chicago's west and southwest sides. LCHC provides services from 5 geographic locations, employs 500 people, and provides 200,000 clinical visits of care per year and 200,000 fitness center visits for 54,000 people.
Bruce began his career in 1984 providing administrative leadership at Community Health Centers similar to LCHC in rural Mississippi and then in central Pennsylvania. In 1989, he joined the Children's Hospital of Pittsburgh and advanced through several positions involving the oversight of a variety of hospital operating units with

*primary responsibility for the hospital's ambulatory care programs.
He earned a B.A. degree in sociology from Geneva College and an
M.H.A. from the University of Pittsburgh. Bruce and his wife,
Kathryn, have three children. They reside in Chicago's North
Lawndale neighborhood, one-half block from LCHC's main site on
Ogden Avenue.*

STRATEGIES
OF HEALTHCARE

CHAPTER

21

WHERE DOES HEALTH COME FROM?
A CHALLENGE TO COMPLETE THE U.S. MEDICAL SYSTEM

David Hilton

It has taken me years to learn where health comes from. When I finished medical school, my wife, Laveta, and I decided that we weren't going to follow the path most medical school graduates follow – seeking prestige, power, and money. We believed that if we committed ourselves to God and let God lead us, we would find much greater satisfaction. To this very day, we have never had any reason to regret that decision.

So we applied to a mission board. I had no idea what I was doing! One of the pearls that I learned from that experience is not to worry if you don't know everything that you think you need to know. The most important thing is to do what the Lord wants you to do. The mission board sent Laveta and me to a missionary hospital in Nigeria, three hundred miles from the nearest town and seventy miles from the nearest road. It was a hospital with one hundred and ten beds, staffed by three European nurses, Laveta, and me – the only medical facility for a quarter of a million people. I arrived, fresh out of medical training, ready to work.

During those years, I did all the heroics that medical missionaries are supposed to do. Our staff saw three to four hundred outpatients per day. Even though we only had a little over a hundred beds in the hospital, we had patients on mats on the floor between beds most of the time. I did six major operations a day, six days a week. In between operations, I saw inpatients. At the end of each day, I trained Nigerians to do some of the things that I was doing because it wasn't possible for us to do everything that needed to be done. We trained medical assistants to see outpatients, do much of the inpatient work, and even to do some surgical procedures. I enjoyed all of that. It was an exciting medical practice – every day I saved the lives of several people.

As time went on, however, it became clear to me that nothing was changing. At the end of the ten years that I spent at that hospital, it was obvious that the situation was not any different than it was when I started. In spite of all our activity, there were just as many sick people as there were when we started. People would come in with malaria, be treated, go home, and get malaria again. People would come in with schistosomiasis, get treatment, go home and get schistosomiasis again. We were on a treadmill. I was able to write fantastic letters about the things we were doing. I could send the mission board incredible statistics. But it was clear that nothing was changing. I didn't feel good about that – and so we left.

That hospital is still there. Doctors are still doing the same good things that I was doing. That is good, because that kind of work needs to be done. When people are sick, they need to be treated. But I felt that God was calling me to begin to deal with some of the root causes of the illnesses that I was seeing again and again.

I joined a program in a neighboring state, operated by the Church of the Brethren, which was attempting to deal with the root causes of the sea of diseases around them. I can speak with glowing terms about this program because I didn't design it – I got involved after it was already functioning. The focus of this program was training communities by training community developers. These community developers would go into a village, explain that the mission didn't have money or personnel to build a clinic or provide them with a nurse or doctor, and tell them that if they were interested they could be trained to solve their own health problems.

In Nigeria, as in many other developing countries, the government promised free healthcare. Corruption, however, makes this promise of medical assistance improbable, and in some cases, impossible. And because of politics playing a major role in the medical arena, people in some rural areas think of health not as a personal responsibility, but rather as a governmental one. Nigerians in certain provinces will wait for officials to act upon health issues, and if the government does not respond to crises soon enough or at all, families move to different villages and try their luck there.

In many villages, however, people did want to learn how to improve, and take full responsibility for, their health. The community developer would visit these villages several times to help people get interested in their health problems and the cause of their illnesses. When people began to ask what they could do to get rid of the health problems that were devastating their communities, the community developer would suggest that they choose a man and a woman to be their health promoters, and that these people enroll in a three-month course.

We taught them primarily with stories, showing how other communities had eliminated the causes of their illness. After three months, they went back to their own communities as health promoters, using the same techniques to get people interested in their own health and then actually doing something about the causes of disease in their community. I saw the health of these communities revolutionized – and they did it by themselves. It was exciting to see that happen.

At that time in Nigeria, the four major causes of death and disease were malaria, diarrhea dehydration, malnutrition, and complications related to pregnancy. The government in Nigeria had started draining the swamps and spraying houses, but it ran out of funds and said that it could do nothing about malaria. Health promoters proved that to be untrue. They would teach mothers to buy one tablet of Daraprim a month (at about one penny each) and give it to their child. These mothers virtually eliminated deaths from malaria in their communities.

If you have been in the tropics, you know that the pediatric wards are filled with children getting IV fluids to replace fluids lost in diarrheal dehydration. The sad thing is that most of the children with diarrheal dehydration never make it to the hospitals – they die at home. The standard solution was to admit them to the hospital and give them IV fluids, but this wasn't making a dent in the problems. Our approach was to teach mothers to mix certain proportions of sugar, salt, and water, and give it to their child as soon as he or she developed diarrhea. This prevented death from dehydration. This medicine began to be called "the miracle medicine" in Lardin Gabas, a province in northeastern Nigeria, because it virtually eliminated death from diarrheal dehydration.

> *People immediately think that the healthcare system is where health comes from, but they do not realize that health is something inherent in everybody. It has to be protected, developed, and guarded by the individual.*

The government's solution for malnutrition was to import fish meal from Brazil and surplus powdered milk from the United States, and to try to distribute them among fifty million children. This could only solve a tiny portion of the problem – and it created a dependency on other countries. Our solution was to train mothers to grind peanuts, which are grown in Nigeria as a cash crop, into peanut butter and mix this into the porridge that every family ate. Fed to the children from four months to five years old, this eliminated malnutrition among the children of these communities. The mothers did it themselves when given the appropriate information, after asking us how to eliminate malnutrition in their community.

The solution to problem pregnancies in most countries is to train obstetricians to run prenatal clinics – without realizing that there is no way that every pregnant woman can see an obstetrician. We trained the woman health promoters to run prenatal clinics in their own villages. Most of the health promoters were illiterate, but they could determine a high-risk pregnancy and refer the mother to the hospital. They could deliver a low-risk pregnancy at home and cut the umbilical cord with a razor blade that could be bought at the local market.

What we have in our country is not a healthcare system. It is focused on disease, not health. It is focused on cure, not care.

As you can see, the four leading causes of disease and death in these communities were eliminated by the people themselves. No clinic was built. No doctor or nurse was required. This is what I refer to when I talk about community-based healthcare: enabling people to take their lives and their health into their own hands.

I would live in these communities for several weeks at a time, to see how the health promoters were working. Many times I would sit with the elders of a community and talk about the changes they had seen. The most frequent response was to say with great pride, "We haven't had a child die in our village since our health promoter came back." And this is a part of the world where less than fifty percent of the children made it to age five. It was very exciting to be involved in this kind of work.

After three years, the Gongola state government in Nigeria appointed me the medical officer for primary care in that state. They asked me to implement this type of system for four million people, in the midst of government regulations and bureaucracy. These were the most frustrating years of my life. The Ministry of Health promised me anything that I needed but I didn't get anything during that year. But because the people were doing it themselves, we were able to work through that system, and health promoters were telling stories in every village in Gongola. The people in that state were beginning to take responsibility for their own health.

I then came back to the United States, and for six years was in private practice in an affluent community in Wisconsin. For six years after that, I was the doctor for the Seminole Indians in Florida. During those twelve years, it became obvious to me that the United States needed community-based healthcare just as desperately as Nigeria or any third-world country. There is no place in the world where people are more dependent on doctors and medicine and hospitals for their health. No matter where I go in the States, as soon as I mention health, people begin to think about the healthcare system – doctors, medicines, hospitals. People immediately think that the healthcare system is where health comes from, but they do not realize that health is something inherent in everybody. It has to be protected, developed, and guarded by the individual. Doctors, hospitals, and medicines are necessary, but that is not where health comes from.

In the United States, we have a disease-cure system. We talk about healthcare providers as if health is a commodity that can be packaged and delivered. Everything revolves around the doctor. People depend on doctors for their health. The prevailing belief is that you don't have to worry about what you eat or what you do; if you get sick, the doctor will make you well again.

Millions of dollars are spent on curing patients, but almost nothing is spent on preventing illness. Doctors are paid for people to be sick. Why would we be interested in keeping people well? Not long ago, I heard a Christian pediatrician do a presentation on otitis media (inflammation of the inner ear). In his introduction, he said, "I always love to see winter come because there is a lot more otitis media and my patient load goes up and my income increases." The more sick people there are, the more money we make.

When I worked among the Seminole Indians, I learned a lot more than I taught. Every chance I had, I snuck out of the clinic to visit with an older medicine man. I learned more about health and healing from that Indian medicine man than I ever learned in medical school. The Seminoles see illness as an imbalance of a person's world. They see the human being as a triangle, with body, mind, and spirit. When one of these is out of balance with the rest of the triangle, we have "dis-ease." The medicine man's role is to assist the patient in restoring his or her balance or "ease."

Death is not the enemy, as it is in our system. Many Seminole Indians told me that you haven't really lived until you've died, since death is an important part of life. I saw many Seminole Indians die well, with their family around them. They don't spend hundreds and thousands of dollars to fight death. In the disease-cure system we are taught in medical school, death is the enemy. Our role is to save lives. We have set ourselves up for failure because everybody is going to die!

Our role as physicians should be to help people live. I am convinced that community-based healthcare can work in the United States. I have a vision for helping people in this country – not only poor people, but all people – to take their lives and their health into their own hands.

The death rate in children under fifteen had been dropping for almost sixty years before immunizations and antibiotics were available. We often think that we, as medical professionals, are the ones who have saved the children, but an increase in the standard of living reduced the infant morality far more than immunizations and antibiotics. This is not to say that immunizations and antibiotics are not good. They are good, and they have further reduced the death rate, but they are relatively recent arrivals. As we look at the infant mortality and the child mortality rates in this country, where can we most effectively direct our efforts? How can we evaluate what we are doing and what we should be doing?

What we have in our country is not a healthcare system. It is focused on disease, not health. It is focused on cure, not care. And there is no system – we have hospitals in areas where they are not needed, and we have other areas that we label "underserved." As the Scriptures say, "All the people did what was right in their own eyes."[1] If somebody thinks there is a need for a clinic here, they build a clinic here. If somebody else thinks there is a need for a hospital here, they build a hospital. There is no system. For the sake of simplicity, I am going to call this disease-cure, nonsystem level of the healthcare system.

Now there is nothing wrong with curing people. If that is what God has called you to, I say, "Praise the Lord. Hallelujah!" Some are needed to cure sick people. But since curing sick people is not

> *The role of every health worker is to pass on knowledge to people so that they can take responsibility for their own health.*

the total way to deal with health problems, God is calling others and giving them vision to complete the system.

A second level in this medical system is community-oriented healthcare. We are still focused on curing people, and we are still centering on the medical professionals as the deliverers of care, but we are involving people from the community. We are getting their opinions and enlisting their aid. Most inner-city clinics and most private practices that do not involve the community fit into this category. Community-oriented healthcare that will involve the community and cure sick people is badly needed. If it is your calling to establish and operate such a clinic, I say, "Hallelujah! Praise the Lord!" We need people who will get involved in this kind of ministry.

The third level is community-based healthcare, something that is radically different from the situation in which we live. Community-based healthcare involves going into a community without an agenda, with nothing more than a desire to enable that community to solve their problems. By asking questions of people and by observing what is happening in that community, a community developer can begin to understand what the concerns of the people are and help the people think about eliminating the causes of those problems. The goal is to develop a plan that will eliminate the causes of disease from their community. But the key is not to tell people what to do, but to empower people – not to deliver information and supplies to people, but to facilitate people in doing what they need to do for themselves. Poor people may be uneducated, but that does not mean they are senseless.

In community-based healthcare, every health worker is a teacher. The primary function of every health worker is to pass on knowledge to others. In Lardin Gabas, we had a rule that no health worker could do anything that he or she could teach somebody else to do. That meant that I didn't do anything but teach – because there was nothing that I did that I couldn't teach somebody else to do. After all, the Latin word for doctor means 'teacher,' something that our disease nonsystem has forgotten. The role of every health worker is to pass on knowledge to people so that they can take responsibility for their own health.

In Jamkhed, India, I had tears in my eyes when a five-year old girl told a group of farmers in a farmer's club how to deliver a baby. She sang a little song and went through all the motions of delivery. This five-year old girl even told them how to breathe into the baby's mouth if it didn't breathe right away. In this program in India, everybody teaches what they know to everybody they can. People take responsibility for their own health and are not dependent on some doctor with a beeper, sitting and waiting until he or she comes. That is community-based healthcare.

One sacred premise of community-based healthcare is not to create dependency. We are to enable people to take responsibility for their own health. Whenever we plan, we have to ask ourselves whether this is going to cause people to depend on someone else for their health or whether it is going to enable them to take responsibility. This is one of the foundations of community-based healthcare.

Community-based healthcare doesn't depend on institutions. As much as can possibly be done is done in the community should be done in and by the community. We don't depend on high technology. We have a different way of looking at who is an inpatient and who is an outpatient. When working in community-based healthcare, an inpatient is one who is in the community, and an outpatient is one who is out of the community. The idea is to keep the person an inpatient in their community for as long as possible, so that patients are not alienated from their community.

When I was working with the Seminole Indians, I worked with a fifteen-year old girl who was in a car accident. She had a broken arm, a broken pelvis, and a broken leg. I had to admit her to the hospital.

They stripped off her clothes and took away everything she owned. They put her in traction in a room with bare walls. She was totally removed from her environment, yet we expected her to get well. We removed all of her emotional supports that she had in her life. When I wrote on her chart that this patient was to have Indian medicine, the nurses started wondering if they were going to build a fire on the floor and dance around it. But when the Indian medicine man came to see her with a little bottle of liquid with herbs, leaves, and bark, and did a little ceremony with that girl, he reestablished her with her community. I am convinced that had a lot more to do with her getting well than anything else I wrote on her chart while she was in the hospital.

This is community-based healthcare – doing medicine where people are and where they live.

This is community-based healthcare – doing medicine where people are and where they live. This is not second-rate medicine; a stopgap for the poor until they can get something better. This is real healthcare, and we've got to become convinced of that.

After my six years of practice in an affluent community in Wisconsin, I am convinced that they need community-based healthcare just as desperately as the poor do, but they don't realize it. For fifteen years, the surgeon general has been saying that eighty-five percent of the disease in this country is preventable. People don't need to have strokes. People don't need to have coronaries. People don't need to have their legs amputated because of diabetes. All of these things are preventable. We are taught to say, "Don't worry what you eat, drink, or smoke. When you get sick, the doctor will fix you." That is a lie. The people in this country need to learn to take responsibility for their own health. Because churches are one of the few remaining viable communities, I believe that the churches in this country can help. You are the people who have the key to solving the healthcare crisis in this country. A health promoter doing participatory learning can enable people to stay well.

The fourth level in this healthcare system is spirit-generated health – something we are hearing more and more about in the medical journals. While I was in family practice in Wisconsin, one of my patients was a young woman in her thirties. She had rheumatoid arthritis and was in so much pain that she had to quit her job as a medical technician. The first time I saw Martha, she was in a wheelchair. She was on the most powerful medicines available for rheumatoid arthritis, including steroids and antidepressants, but she was not able to walk or even pick anything up with her hands.

The second time I saw Martha, I asked her, in an open-ended way, what was going on in her life. She began to tell me a story of how, as a teenager, she had gone to bed with her boyfriend. She awoke the next morning in horror, fear, and anxiety, but she had no one with whom she dared share this story. She had lived alone with her guilt for fifteen years. She had become increasingly crippled, until she had to quit her job. As Martha told this story to me, and as I listened sympathetically, her hands began to straighten out! We were able to gradually reduce her medications and finally stop them completely. She started to walk again, and eventually went back to work.

As I listened and showed that I was concerned about her well-being, Martha was cured. Those of you who have been in practice for any length of time have seen patients like this. Now we are beginning to see articles in medical literature indicating that our immune system is more sensitive to what we are thinking, what we are feeling, what we believe, than it is to germs and cancer cells. It is becoming increasingly apparent that what is going on in our lives in actually what determines our health.

There is a study from England on arteriosclerosis in rabbits. Some rabbits were fed high doses of cholesterol. As you would expect, they all got arteriosclerosis, but one subsection didn't get nearly as much as the others. The only difference they could find was that this subsection was being taken care of by a laboratory technician who took her rabbits out of the cages each day and petted them. So they repeated the experiment and got exactly the same results – the group that was petted had a lower rate of arteriosclerosis. They corroborated this study by doing T-lymphocyte counts on the rabbits and found that the ones that were petted had a much higher T-lymphocyte count than those that were not.

In another study referred to as the Framingham Heart Study, the original printouts showed that those who go to church have a lower incidence of heart attacks than those who don't. At first, everyone laughed and said that it was a fluke in the studies, but now researchers are reconsidering because their work on the immune system is showing that these are the kinds of things that determine health and disease.

You may have heard of Bernie Seigel, the oncologist surgeon at Yale University. He would receive the cases that no one else wanted to handle. So many of his patients were dying that he got discouraged. Then he decided to start asking them open-ended questions about what was going on in their lives. Some of his patients with cancer discovered for themselves that they were committing suicide with their cancer. Even more surprising, they discovered that, one of two things happened. One group decided that they did not want to die and found some other way to deal with their problems. In those people, the cancers disappeared completely – what scientists call a "spontaneous remission." The other group said, "Yes, that's right. I do want to die. I have had enough of life." Even in cases where people had been hanging on for months, those patients died within hours.

It is becoming increasingly clear that the idea that there are psychosomatic diseases and "real" diseases is a myth. There is no separation – all diseases have a lot to do with what's going on in our lives.

What is the significance of this for us? Everything in the world! What does the gospel deal with if not with what is going on in our daily lives? It did not take four years of medical education for me to sit and listen sympathetically to Martha as her arthritis was healed. Any person with the love of Christ in his or her heart can spend time listening to people. The beautiful thing about this is that it liberates health from healthcare professionals and frees all Christians to be healers. What is the church if not a group of caring, loving, sharing people who support each other when bad things are going on in our lives? There is a strong connection between sin, broken relationships, and disease, for what is sin if not broken relationships with God and each other?

It is well known that people who have lost a spouse in the last two years have a much higher incidence of cancer than those who haven't. Where is the community who is rallying around the person who has lost a spouse to care, to nurture, to love?

In the area of addictions, the most successful treatment program is Alcoholics Anonymous. A.A. is nothing more than a group of people who get together, tell their life stories and bare their souls, who care about each other, who support each other, who love each other, and who don't take any pretense or excuses from each other. They become well. Why can't the church be that kind of community?

In church after church, if a teenage girl becomes pregnant, she is secretly scuttled off to seclusion. Or if a man becomes an alcoholic, he is slipped out the back door to some treatment center without letting anyone know what is happening. What a shame! The healing centers of the world are the churches, the congregations, and the small communities of Christians.

Real evangelism occurs when a community of Christians is living out the gospel so vitally in their lives that people are seeking them out to ask, "What is going on in here? I want to be a part of that." You can read all the books you want on how to do street evangelism, or how to do urban evangelism, but if you are not living out the gospel in your life, if you're not helping each other, it is useless.

In the fifth chapter of James, we read, "Are any among you sick? They should call for the elders of the church and have them pray over the sick, anointing them with oil in the name of the Lord. The prayer of faith will save the sick, and the Lord will raise them up; and anyone who has committed sins will be forgiven."[2]

In 2 Chronicles, God speaks to the Hebrew people and says, "If my people who are called by my name humble themselves, pray, seek my face, and turn from their wicked ways, then I will hear from heaven, and will forgive their sin and heal their land."[3] That is the challenge for us.

I want to leave you with an old story, one you have probably already heard. A man was mountain climbing. He was inching along a narrow ledge over a sheer precipice when he slipped and fell off the edge. As he was falling, he grabbed onto a small tree protruding from the cliff. He hung onto that tree, several hundred feet above the valley floor. Not knowing what to do, in desperation he shouted, "Is anybody up there?" A voice answered, "Yes." He asked, "Well, who is it?" The answer came back, "It's God." The man pleaded, "Help me get out of here!" The voice responded, "OK. Let go of that branch." There was a long silence. Finally the man asked, "Is there anybody else up there?"

That is our story. We hang on to our medical education. We hang on to our medicines. We hang on to our professional abilities. We hang on to so many things – yet we know where the power is. We know what God wants to do in the world – if we can just let go.

David Hilton, MD, was a primary health consultant with extensive experience in fifty-eight countries, and served on the board of CCHF. His life experiences include working in a remote rural area of northern Nigeria; practicing Family Medicine in Wisconsin; serving as the physician for the Seminole Tribe of Florida; being a staff member of the Christian Medical Commission in Geneva, Switzerland; and serving as the editor of Contact, a bi-monthly religion and health publication published in six languages in 130 countries. He has done consulting in 58 countries on five continents. At Emory University, he was an adjunct professor of International Health and special assistant to the university chaplain, working with international students and students in the schools of Medicine and Public Health. Dr. Hilton lived in Clarkston, GA, with his wife, Laveta, a pianist and international musicologist. The couple had two daughters and one son. Dr. Hilton died in August, 2008, of complications of non-Hodgkin's lymphoma at the age of 76.

CHAPTER

22

LEARNING TO PRAY FOR HEALING

Steve Hawthorne

A woman in labor entered the ER where I was a medical student, saying her bag of waters had broken. I checked her and found the umbilical cord coming down in front of the baby's head. With each contraction, the pulsations in the cord slowed to vanishing, then recovered as her pain eased. I called out for an emergency cesarean, and kept my hand inside the birth canal to keep pressure off the cord. Only when she was on the table in the operating room did I withdraw my hand, and run to scrub to assist the surgeon.

The anesthetist gave us the nod, but before making his incision, and to my great distress, the surgeon paused to acknowledge in prayer our dependence on God and ask his help for a good outcome. I nearly snatched the scalpel from his hand before he was done. What was he thinking by waiting any longer? Thick meconium! Fetal distress! Risk of stillbirth! Risk of brain damage! Get the baby out!

That night I asked myself the question: In what sense am I a "Christian physician?"

Yes, I am a Christian. I believe Jesus is God become man. I believe his death removed my sin and reconciled me to God. Believing parents nurtured my faith, as did an evangelical church and a Christian college. In these circles I learned to pray.

I learned to administer healing in a state university. Prayer was not part of my training there. My professors approached patients with compassion, but with no expectation of divine intervention. Healing depended on the proper application of the scientific method.

Revisiting the example of Jesus is the best way to begin to unite the physical and spiritual realms. Jesus carried people's illnesses as well as their sins.

My shock at the surgeon's taking time to pray in that emergency revealed to me the extent to which I had unwittingly compartmentalized my faith. I acknowledged God's redemptive work in people's souls, but simply did not consider God in regard to their physical problems. I practiced medicine exactly like my Muslim, Hindu, or atheist friends that trained with me. Only in how I spent my nonworking hours did my Christianity set me apart.

The expression "Christian physician" had become for me an oxymoron: a combination of incongruous words. Thus began my quest to integrate my secular, scientific profession of healing with my faith in God, who actively sustains all aspects of his creation. I began by asking myself:

Why do I feel uncomfortable praying for healing?
Because my scientific education makes me skeptical. My heart is Christian but my mind is a product of my culture. My studies convinced me that natural laws of cause and effect are the only decent way to understand reality.

How did I come to take for granted the idea that God does not intervene in the natural order? Our society makes it possible for people of different religious faiths to live peacefully together by making science our common language for public debate, and relegating religion to our private lives. Though a Christian, I unconsciously came to restrict my faith to church on Sundays. On weekdays I lived by the principles I learned in school, turning to secular science for answers as to why we get sick or why a tornado struck. My worldview allowed God free reign in the spiritual domain but did not expect to see him act in the physical domain outside the laws of nature he established.

Because I feel that praying for healing is "putting God to the test."[1] Not only is that something that we are not supposed to do, but also if I asked for a patient's healing and nothing happened, I wouldn't know what to think of God. I (or they) might lose faith in a loving, all-powerful God. It is safer not to ask.

How do I change my way of thinking?
Revisiting the example of Jesus is the best way to begin to unite the physical and spiritual realms. Jesus carried people's illnesses as well as their sins.[2] Jesus, the image of the invisible God, consistently viewed sickness as an enemy to rebuke, a work of the devil to undo. I learned from watching Jesus that God delights in dispelling pain, restoring sanity, straightening crooked limbs, opening blind eyes, feeding hungry people and forgiving sinners.[3] God revealed himself in Jesus as being on the side of wholeness in spirit, mind, and body. Jesus challenged poor people to believe the Good News of a loving God, who forgave their sins and healed their hurts.

Did Jesus expect his followers to stay involved in healing?
Jesus set an example for his followers, and then he gave them authority to heal – first to the twelve[4] and later to the seventy-two.[5] After his resurrection, he repeated that they were to continue his work in the power of the Holy Spirit. In Mark's version of the Great Commission, Jesus says that "those who believe... will place their hands on sick people and they will recover."[5]

In the book of Acts, Peter, Stephen, Philip, Ananias and Paul all healed people as Jesus did.[6] And for the next several centuries, churchmen such as Clement, Justin, Tertullian, and Cyprian continue to mention healings as part of normal church life in their time.[7]

In the apostle Paul's first letter to the Christians living in Corinth, he mentions that some in the church received from the Holy Spirit the ability to heal for the common good. I grew up thinking the gifts of healing, miracles, and speaking in unknown languages were signs and wonders necessary to impress people in the first century of the Christian era with the power of the gospel.[8] Once the church was established, I understood that God withdrew these gifts.

But today as I reread the section on gifts in 1 Corinthians 12:27 through 13:13, I see that none of the gifts disappears until "perfection comes," which I understand to mean until our Lord Jesus returns and we are forever in his presence. We only lose what we fail to use.

It is impressive to review the invitations – commands even – to ask God for what we need. Here are a few of them:

Ask and it will be given to you.
Ask the Lord of the harvest.
Ask and you will receive and your joy will be complete.
Ask God, who gives generously to all without finding fault.
You do not have because you do not ask God.
If we ask anything according to his will, he hears us.
Jesus sums up: "So I say to you: Ask!"[9]

Thus asking becomes an act of obedience. God promises his people, "I know you have needs. Ask me for them and I will supply." The starting place in praying for healing is gaining the confidence to ask, trusting wholly in his concern for our well-being; possessing the assurance that asking for healing is in accordance with God's will.

How do I pray for the sick?

The Holy Spirit gives gifts of healing and discernment to the Body of Christ to be God's means for restoring people to wholeness – whether of a physical, emotional, relational or spiritual kind.[10] A service of healing in a local church based on the principles of James 5:13-16 is the ideal place for a team to minister to hurting people in the presence of Jesus. (Upon request, the author will send suggestions for getting started in a church-based healing ministry, which go beyond the scope of this article.)

In praying for sick people one-on-one, whether in a medical office or in homes, the Lord's Prayer gives a helpful pattern. In his ministry, Jesus showed just what "May your will be done on earth"[11] looks like: the sick are healed, widows are helped and justice is done. When I pray "Your will be done," I mean, "Through me, an agent working with God to accomplish his purposes. In my prayer on another's behalf, I make a conscious contribution to the unfolding of the course of events in my corner of the world toward life, love, joy, and peace. I pray as God's fellow-worker, asking for what is needed for the joint work.

"Give us today our daily bread" is an invitation to ask God with confidence for the food, the strength, the wisdom, and the health needed to do our task of bringing honor to his name and extending his kingdom.

"Forgive us our debts as we also have forgiven our debtors." The act of forgiving ends the chronic anger, resentment, and bitterness that acts as a cancer to the soul.

"Deliver us from the evil one" is a prayer for rescue from all the ways and works of Satan – from sickness as well as from sin.[12]

In my office, I use my experience and the medicines at my disposal to aid healing. With willing patients, I take their hand and pray, seeing them as God created them to be – his image-bearers, filled with shalom. I pray with con-

In my prayer on another's behalf, I make a conscious contribution to the unfolding of the course of events in my corner of the world toward life, love, joy, and peace.

fidence, believing God's will is to restore to wholeness persons who ask. I also pray with thanksgiving, knowing that in his sovereignty he can turn sickness to useful purposes in our lives. Whether and when the person recovers depends on God, not on my own powers. I don't change God's mind by prayer, but cooperate with God's providence.

What happens if I pray for healing and the person stays sick?
This is a common situation, even in Scripture. Jesus prayed in Gethsemane to avoid death, but God did not grant his request. The apostle Paul was a healer, yet illness did not disappear from his life or

those of his companions.

> *As you know, it was because of an illness that I first preached the gospel to you.*
> *Epaphroditus is distressed because you heard he was ill.*
> *There was given me a thorn in my flesh, a messenger of Satan to torment me.*
> *Stop drinking only water, and use a little wine because of your... frequent illnesses.*
> *Erastus stayed in Corinth and I left Trophimus sick in Miletus.*[13]

The writer to the Hebrews says something very startling about Jesus: "God, for whom and through whom everything was made, chose to bring many children into glory. And it was only right that he should make Jesus, through his suffering, a perfect leader, fit to bring them into their salvation."

The experience of suffering played a role in making the Son of God "perfect," or "complete, mature" (Gk. telios). Whatever else this means, it is clear that suffering can have an extremely important and beneficial effect in the life of Christ's followers. It can draw us into closer dependence upon God, cause us to review the state of our lives, and strengthen our faith that God will never leave us nor forsake us. An enforced rest can get our attention or redirect us; we may experience the care of the Body of Christ for the first time.[13]

Paul's handling of his experience with the "thorn in the flesh" described in 2 Corinthians 12:7-10 is very instructive:

- He was not surprised that a Christian should develop a physical affliction.
- He saw the affliction as something evil, a "messenger of Satan," not a blessing from God.
- His first response was to pray that it leave him, to ask God for healing. It was normal for him to pray for the removal of sickness rather than its acceptance.
- His own prayer for healing went unanswered, though he had prayed successfully for others.
- He gained new insights into God's grace through the

experience of suffering.
- He had discernment about when he should stop asking for healing, while continuing to trust.

We believe that it is God's will for all to be saved and to come to a knowledge of the truth,[14] and so we continue to pray in faith for unsaved loved ones for years without seeing the salvation of that person. In the same way, we can persist in praying for healing without doubting God's power or willingness to heal, like Abraham, whose faith did not waver through twenty-five years of waiting.[15]

I needed to learn to pray for healing in order to bridge the compartments I'd made, and invite Jesus to participate in my healing profession. But I've also learned that praying just for healing may be asking for too little. The big request, springing from our deepest desire, is to know God, enjoy him and experience the comfort of his presence. And often, it is in trials that this happens.

When we are convinced of God's good intentions toward us, we can pray, "Lord, I want to be healed, but I've discovered that I want you even more than I want health. You decide how I can be made complete in my knowledge of you – as an invalid (or a widow, or an insomniac, etc.) or as healthy." Instead of insisting that I must have this one thing done for me, I free God to act on my behalf in any way he chooses.

What is the take-home message?
We have God's permission to ask for healing! When we get sick, remember the many ways that he invites us to ask for healing. If, as we ask for healing, we relinquish our lives for his glory, surrendered to him for the extension of his kingdom, we may see God turn the experience into a good we didn't anticipate.

When our children are sick, let's pray with them while we give them Tylenol, so they come to rely on "the LORD, who heals you,"[16] not just on the pill.

If our local church or churches in the community in which we minister do not have a healing service, let's encourage forming one.

Let's rejoice that God loves us! We believe that God both wants and has the power not only to heal but also to reveal himself to us in intimate ways.

Let's resist the atheistic patterns in our thinking. Many of us, because of our training and background, simply do not believe that God intervenes directly in people's lives, nor do we have any evidence from our own experiences that he does. We have lived our lives with such a view for so long that it will be a struggle for us to think otherwise.

Let's renounce the sin of King Asa, who "was afflicted with a disease in his feet. Though his disease was severe, even in his illness he did not seek help from the Lord, but only from the physicians."[17] Consider how Isaiah 31:1 sounds with these substitutions:

Woe to those who go down to [doctors] for help, who rely on [pharmacists], who trust in the multitude of their [hospitals] and in the great strength in their [medicines], but do not look to the Holy One of Israel, or seek help from the Lord.

Let's affirm that "God was pleased to have all his fullness dwell in Jesus and through him to reconcile to himself all things, whether things on earth or things in heaven, by making peace through his blood, shed on the cross."[18] This reconciliation extends to our mortal bodies as well as our sinful souls. This same Lord, who was so quick to heal while he was on earth, now sits at the right hand of God, holding all power in heaven and earth. Let's not limit the present exercise of God's power by failing to ask him for healing wherever we see it needed, leaving the results of our prayers entirely in his loving hands. "Those who say they live in God should live their lives as Jesus did."[19]

For Further Reading

- Graf, Jonathan L., ed. Healing: The Three Great Classics on Divine Healing, Christian Publications, 1992. (A compilation of The Ministry of Healing by A.J. Gordon; Divine Healing by Andrew Murray and The Gospel of Healing by A.B. Simpson in one volume.)

- MacNutt, Francis, Ph.D. Healing, Notre Dame, IN: Ave Maria Press, 1999.
- Pearson, Mark A, Christian Healing: A Practical and Comprehensive Guide, Grand Rapids, MI: Chosen Books, 1995.
- Lewis, C.S., Letters to Malcolm, Chiefly on Prayer, New York: Harcourt Brace & C0., 1963.
- Marshall, Catherine, Beyond Our Selves, New York: McGraw-Hill Book Company, 1961
- Miller, Darrow L., Discipling Nations, Colorado Springs, CO: YWAM, 1998

Praying for sick children and adults:
Lord Jesus Christ, Good Shepherd of the sheep, you gather the lambs in your arms and carry them in your bosom: We commend to your loving care this child (name). Relieve his pain, guard him from all danger, restore to him your gifts of gladness and strength, and raise him up to a life of service to you. Hear us, we pray, for your dear (name's) sake. Amen.

Almighty God and Father, you strengthen the weak and comfort the suffering. Have mercy on us and hear us, we pray. Give your power to (name) that her sickness may be turned to health, and her sorrow to joy and peace. Fill her with your grace that she may serve you with her whole heart in the knowledge of your love for her. This we ask in the name of your Son, our Lord Jesus, Amen.

Steve Hawthorne, MD, received his B.A. degree in Biblical Studies from Wheaton College in 1981, and his M.D. from the University of Illinois in 1985. After finishing a residency in Family Practice, he and his wife, Mary, went to Bolivia where they have been working since 1989 as medical missionaries with SIM International among the Quechua people.

CHAPTER

23

MOTIVATING THE POOR TO MAKE LIFESTYLE CHANGES

Carolyn Parks

I am convinced that poor people are concerned about their health. I am also convinced that the cycle of poverty and the nature of the systems that they have to deal with tend to hinder their dealing with their health.

We need to look at some of the barriers both in the cycle of poverty and in the structure and nature of social agencies that tend to hinder a poor person's development of lifestyle changes.

I'm not convinced, however, that we can actually motivate anyone to change. Motivation is an internal, intrinsic value, and we can do very little to motivate people or to make them want to come to the place of changing their lifestyles. What we can do is try to provide them with opportunities that may get them to the point where they will become motivated to make changes. I think it's important to make this distinction. We can help individuals in the process of development to become motivated, but we ourselves cannot provide them the motivation to make behavior changes.

Seven out of ten leading causes of death in the U.S. are related to lifestyle issues. Some of the literature estimates that the lifestyle factor in the leading causes of death is as high as fifty percent – and possibly higher. It therefore makes sense for us to look at the issues of nutrition, weight control, exercise, stress management, mental health, and substance abuse in poor communities so that we can help people come to a place where they can alter some of these behaviors.

The missing link in our system is that individuals are getting lots of knowledge but no skills on how to put this knowledge into practice.

When we talk about lifestyle changes, we need to remember that these behaviors have developed over years, often beginning in infancy. If a patient with hypertension who has been on a high sodium diet for the past fifty years came into my office and I told him or her to stop using salt within a month, I would be giving that patient an impossible task. The behavior was developed over years, and it is going to take a significant amount of time to reverse it. In addition, eating behaviors are also deeply rooted in culture, family, and the cycle of poverty. The strategies that we develop have to be supported by the cultural, familial, and social backgrounds of the individual.

It is not sufficient to give patient information. How many times have you heard health professionals say, "I told them, and I told them, and I told them." Information is not enough. The literature tells us that the people of this era are more knowledgeable about their health than their predecessors ever were, yet they are still not making lifestyle changes.

The missing link in our system is that individuals are getting lots of knowledge but no skills on how to put this knowledge into practice. In relation to hypertension, doctors, nurses, and health educators may tell folks they need to lower their sodium intake, but few give their patients strategies on how to do this. They are not teaching people how to read food labels to determine salt content. They are not telling them how to go to a store and compare the sodium contents, in milligrams, of various products. They are not teaching them about hidden sodium in foods and strategies for lowering sodium in cooking methods. This is all vital information if we are going to teach people how to lower their sodium intake. It is not enough to provide individuals with information; they also need skills to implement that information.

The most difficult link in this process is to provide a positive internal and external environment in which the person can operate. This is a particular problem in poor communities where people are getting the information and

Christians are particularly guilty of violating poor communities by walking in with our own agendas, our own issues, and our own needs without considering the people and the culture of that community.

possibly the skills, but they do not have an environment in which to carry out those skills. As a result, they either implement lifestyle changes on a very limited basis or do not implement them at all.

We need to come up with some creative ways to address this problem. Let's say that you have been called to serve in China. You are very excited about the opportunity. What would you do? What are some things that you would do prior to leaving for China? You would probably want to learn a little Chinese. You would probably go to the library and devour every book you could find on China. You would probably make it a point to talk to any Chinese people you knew. You might visit a Chinese church. You would seek out people who have been there. You would pray for hours about this opportunity. You would do all you could to learn about that culture.

Why is it that when we talk about working in a poor community, we don't do such preparation? All too often I hear of people who come into poor communities, set up shop, and tell folks, "We are here to meet all of your problems because we are concerned about you." We would never dream of going to China without doing all we could to prepare ourselves, yet we walk into poor communities with very little or no preparation. Then we get frustrated because the people do not listen to us and do no want to hear what we have to say. Those of us in the Christian community are particularly guilty of violating these poor communities by walking in with our own agendas, our own issues, and our own needs without considering the people and the culture of that community.

It is essential that prior to working in a community, we do all that we can to learn about the culture and understand the people who live there. This is particularly important for white Americans going into minority communities. Whether whites like it or not, they are viewed as part of the system. They are viewed as "the man," and all their good intentions, all their knowledge, all their skills, and all their sincerity does not change that. Moving into a minority community does not change that.

Wherever we work among the poor, we need to build and cultivate relationships. We need to build a knowledge base of that community. Most of us, myself included, have been trained under a white, middle-class system. Most of the approaches and strategies that we learned in our training do not work in poor communities.

The first step is to get to know that community almost as well as you know yourself. Study the community and the individuals in it. Come to understand the culture, what makes the people in the community tick, and what they believe about health. We know that poor people often have different definitions of health and illness than the rest of society. You need to know this information to establish relationships, so that as folks talk with you, you can understand what it is that they are saying.

Social service agencies may have personnel who have some knowledge of a specific area, but they may have very little knowledge about how to communicate that message in a culturally-appropriate and effective way. Most of us have little idea of what we are asking when we ask people to make lifestyle changes.

Have you ever tried to lose fifty or more pounds? Over the last few years, I have lost thirty pounds, so I know what a struggle it is. Have you ever tried to change your diet? Very few of us have, so we do not realize how difficult this is. When we talk about lifestyle changes, we need to remember that most of us have little idea about what we are asking people to do. We will tell them, "You need to lose fifty pounds because your hypertension is out of control," but we have no idea what it takes to lose fifty pounds. We need to offer suggestions in an empathetic way, with the realization that some of the things we are asking people to do are monumental undertakings.

When we go into a particular community with our pre-established agendas and goal, we demonstrate a lack of sensitivity to cultural differences. Very little of our health education literature is culturally- and ethnically-appropriate. In addition, the literacy level of most of the literature in our health clinics is inadequate for the poor communities where we work.

When we go into a particular community with our pre-established agendas and goal, we demonstrate a lack of sensitivity to cultural differences.

We use individual approaches in our health education, but our patients go back home to a community. Most poor communities do not offer the kind of social network or environment that supports many of the changes we recommend. Patients trying to reduce their sodium intake may have difficulty finding low-sodium foods in their grocery stores. They may therefore have to go outside of the community, but if they don't have a car or even a grocery cart to go to a market outside the community, they cannot follow through with this recommendation. The individual approach has limitations. We need to develop alternative strategies.

One of the most prominent barriers in a community of poverty is mistrust – mistrust of you, mistrust of the system, mistrust of what you are telling them. While some of this mistrust is unjustified, most of it is warranted. These individuals have been brutally damaged and dehumanized by the system.

You need to become familiar with the language of poverty, which is another major barrier to making lifestyle changes. I am not referring only to dialects and ethnic languages, but to a language of poverty that is characterized by self-hatred and low levels of self-esteem. Many of the behaviors that we see are self-destructive behaviors, such as a substance abuse and overeating. And of course the high homicide rate among black males illustrates the acting out of self-hatred.

I talk to many providers who get frustrated because people use their services inappropriately. They are frustrated when folks come in with minor problems that really do not require a visit to the doctor. Yet providers don't teach people how to use the system appropriately. They keep coming back with runny noses because we do not provide them with the knowledge and skills they need to use the system properly.

It is not that poor people are apathetic and lazy. I am convinced that they really don't know what we are talking about. When we discuss lifestyles, most don't know what the issue is. It is not a matter of disinterest and laziness; it is a lack of skills. It is well documented that poor people do not know how to view symptoms. Many have no idea that it doesn't make sense for them to come in with a runny nose. They view symptoms differently from the rest of us. They have not been told how to recognize the symptoms of disease.

In fact, many poor people have a totally different concept of health. They tend to have functional definitions of health, primarily in relationship to their jobs. If they can get up for work and deal with their little pains, even though those pains have increased in the last several weeks, they see themselves as healthy. We need to understand these factors when working in poor communities.

What are some general guidelines?

First and foremost, know the community and culture well. Each Hispanic community is different, as is each African American community and each American Indian community. The strategies you develop in one community may not work in another. Your strategies need to be specifically tailored to the special needs and interests of that community.

Once you know a community, you need to accept the community. This is difficult for many of us, since some of the things that the community believes will no doubt counteract what we have been taught and contradict our own value systems. Developers of some of the more successful programs insist that in order for our strategies to work, we must set aside our personal beliefs, accept the values that are found in that community, and be willing to work in concert with them. Many programs are having difficulty because their strategies work against the values of that particular community or culture.

Establish trust. This is critical – particularly as white Americans go into minority communities. Building trust takes a long time. You're going to get many questions about why you are there.

It is critical that you build relationships with the professionals and nonprofessionals who are already working in that community, even before you have established what you will be doing. If you do not build these relationships, the people are not going to listen to what you are saying. It has been frustrating for me to see individuals build relationships with the poor in the community but not with me or other minority professionals who are already working in the community who have expertise in the area that they are trying to target. As the people in the community see you interacting with those they already know and trust, they will see that you are genuinely concerned about the community and are participating with their leaders.

As you come to understand the health beliefs and values, how people get their information, where they get it, and how they interpret it, you will gain insight into the areas that need to be strengthened. You might also target trusted individuals for help in your health education efforts.

We know that poor people use many folk remedies and have many different superstitions. Those that are not harmful need to be left alone. If they are not doing any damage to people, we should leave them alone and let the people continue to practice them.

It is important to involve people from the community at every level of your health efforts, so that you can learn from their insights. I've had people from the community serve on planning committees. They may not say anything during a meeting until at one point they suddenly say, "That ain't gonna work." When I ask them why that is, they'll tell us exactly why a particular idea will not work. I have learned to respect their opinions; the vast majority of the time, they are correct because they know their community much better than we do. We need to involve indigenous community people at every level of our health efforts.

Consciousness-raising is beginning to be viewed as a major tool for helping poor people in this country come to grips with the root causes of the problems in their environment. As we listen to people, we may be able to bring them to the point of beginning to think through why they are in the situation they're in. Then we can ask them what they can begin to do about it.

Risk reduction is controversial. It implies that because we are dealing with so many crucial needs, we need to target those areas of a person's lifestyle where we can have the greatest impact. In poor communities, it may mean teaching folks to do some of these negative things in a safer way.

For example, we usually tell people what foods they should not eat rather than teaching them how to eat various foods that are already part of their diet. One of my concerns is that when we identify foods that are health risks – canned foods, luncheon meats, hot dogs, and hamburgers – most are staples in the diet of poor people. Consequently, there is no way they can comply with our diet lists. Risk reduction then would involve teaching people that if they are going to have a luncheon meat sandwich for lunch, they shouldn't eat hot dogs for dinner. Perhaps we would be more effective if we taught them how to limit their luncheon meat sandwiches, hot dogs, or hamburgers to a certain number each week. Using this strategy to modify their behavior may be more effective. However, this is a sticky subject – particularly when you are addressing issues such as hypertension and diabetes, which are directly related to diet.

The final strategy is using lay health advisors, individuals from the community who have receive some health training, as the major providers of health information in their communities. I am becoming more and more convinced that this is the most effective and cost-efficient way for our messages to be communicated. We already know that the poor don't listen to us, but they might listen to their grandmother or some other trusted community person. I'm looking at ways to target grandmothers, great aunts, and older women in the community who many women naturally go to for help. When we can provide those people with the right kinds of information, we have created a much better way to disseminate information.

We can also target another untapped resource – the church, particularly the smallest storefront churches where the poor attend. It has been my experience that you may get more support from smaller storefront churches that from larger churches, where many activities are already going on.

I have been challenged in the last few years to think of health education in the same way that we think of discipleship – as a major tool for multiplying our efforts. There is no way to reach every person in our communities by ourselves. As we train people from the community who are able to teach others, we can multiply our efforts and get our message across much more effectively.

Carolyn Parks, PhD, is a community health education specialist with over thirty years of experience in health promotion practice and research with African Americans, communities and populations of color, vulnerable populations, and faith-based and community-based organizations. She has been an instructor at many prestigious universities, including University of North Carolina at Chapel Hill, Southern Connecticut State University, and Cleveland State University. Carolyn is currently serving as an HIV/AIDS Prevention Behavioral Scientist at the Center for Disease Control and Prevention in Atlanta, GA.

CHAPTER 24

REDEFINING SUCCESS IN COMMUNITY HEALTH

Sylvia Babu

During my years in ministry among the poor, I have come to redefine several key healthcare concepts. These new definitions evolved over time as I found traditional medical definitions to be dogmatic and static, and felt the need for more dynamic definitions, or what I call "transformational" definitions.

Redefining Community

Community is commonly defined as a group of people living within defined geographical boundaries and sharing a set of common values and beliefs. In my work, I have learned that a group that lives in a given area may not all share the same values and beliefs. People who live in project housing may not even speak to each other. Even the words we use to categorize the poor – words like "marginalized" and "disenfranchised" – while referring to a group of people depict isolation and alienation, not community. The poor are isolated not only from the rest of the population, but from each other as well.

When there is no sense of community, how is it possible to practice community health? As I prepared to apply my public health training in an area where there was no well-defined community, at first I felt paralyzed. What I discovered was that my public health training was still relevant if I chose a different starting point – the concept of neighbor. Though there was no clearly defined community, I could still invite community participation with the goal of community development by relating to one neighbor at a time. No, I cannot measure my accomplishments using population-based data, but I can tell stories of patient encounters that have made a difference for me, and, I think, for them.

Redefining Health
In redefining health, I had to begin by unlearning the "absence of disease" definition I learned in medical school. I am now guided by a concept of health much closer to that defined by the World Health Organization: "a state of complete physical, mental, social, and spiritual well-being."

Each patient encounter reinforces the reality that we must work from this definition if we are to do more than cure minor ailments. Our patients' diseases are due, at least partly, to lifestyles not conducive to health. Dysfunctional families need cures that a purely medical approach cannot provide. So while I still prescribe antibiotics for a child's ear infection, achieving health may require more. It may involve social services to help Mom be compliant with medications and keep follow-up appointments. It may mean providing transportation to and from the clinic. It may call for efforts to provide a smoke-free environment for the child or seeing that the child has adequate heat during winter months.

So far, medical school curricula do not include lessons on working with other agencies involved in the delivery of healthcare services. The social and behavioral aspects of health, while acknowledged, are not adequately covered in classroom lectures. Health continues to be defined in distinctly separate categories of the body and mind.

The poor, even more than the affluent, must spend an inordinate amount of time and energy keeping body, mind, and soul together. Therefore those of us who work among them must learn to look at the whole person if we are to render compassionate service balanced with professional expertise.

Redefining Success

Medical establishments have various ways to measure success: numbers of patients seen, cure rates, numbers "covered" with necessary immunizations, morbidity and mortality statistics, etc. I have found, though, that not all these measures are appropriate in working with the poor. Therefore I now define success not only in these terms, but also in terms of one life on the road to recovery: one mother who enters a drug rehabilitation program, one single mom who goes back to school, one teen who opts for abstinence, one child who grows up in the midst of crime and violence and yet graduates from high school.

Success, in an inner-city clinic like the one where I work, must be a "both/and" success; both a decrease in the standard morbidity and mortality statistics, and evidence of transformed lives. Statistics must be balanced with narratives of recovery. Progress means not only decreased prevalence of disease, but also, movement into the mainstream of society.

My own success is linked to my patients' success. I am human enough to at times envy those who enjoy the greater kind of material "success" I might have had if I followed a more lucrative career choice. I know I could have followed that path. Yet I also know that the greatest freedom is the freedom to obey, and in that freedom, I have found peace.

Sylvia Babu, MD, MPH, obtained her Masters in Public Health from Johns Hopkins University and completed Pediatric Residencies at Children's Mercy Hopital in Kansas City, MO, and Tulane University in New Orleans, LA. In addition, she was a Fellow in Virology at Children's Mercy Hospital in Kansas City, MO, and a Fellow in Infectious Diseases at Wake Forest University, Winston-Salem, NC. Dr. Babu practiced at Children's Healthcare of Atlanta for 13 years. She was an Assistant Professor of Pediatrics at Emory University, as well as University of Maryland School of Medicine. Dr. Babu has also been widely published in professional publications including Journal of *Infectious Disesases, World Health Forum,* and *Practical Manual of Pediatrics. She is currently employed at Kennesaw Pediatrics outside Atlanta, GA.*

CHAPTER 25

NOT IF I HAD KNOWN THE COST

Rosilyn Smith

If I had it to do over again, would I still move into inner-city Philadelphia to live in the shadow of high-rise public housing projects and worship in a store-front church?

No, not if I had known the cost.

I came to Philadelphia fifteen years ago to do my psychiatric residency. It was the only city in the eastern United States that met our educational needs. My husband was looking for a Bible college and I was searching for a position as a psychiatric resident.

During my residency training, I never consciously decided to serve the underprivileged of our city, although I could tell I was on a mission that contrasted sharply with the concerns of my colleagues. They vacationed in the Bahamas, while I spent my time and money supporting my husband as he began a Sunday school ministry to children in North Philadelphia. They spent Saturday afternoons comparison shopping for BMWs, while I passed out Scripture tracts to people living in public housing, often running into clients I had recently met on the psychiatric inpatient unit or in my clinics.

As an African American from a single-parent family, it never occurred to me that there was such a thing as a "ministry to the poor." Inadequate resources, few options, financial and medical crises, drug and alcohol addiction – these were the norm for my friends and neighbors. So as I provided care for my homeless and chronically-ill clients and their families, I was simply practicing the only medicine I knew how to practice.

In my early years in Philadelphia, ministry to the poor was no sweat. Serving others just came naturally. I just wanted to serve God and support my husband as he began to minister to the "down and outers." Unable to find an existing church with a vision for intensive outreach, my husband and I started an exciting new church reaching out to substance abusers, the homeless, and the hungry.

But after three years, brutal reality hit home. Our funding was inadequate to support a church, much less meet the many requests for help. Our education had not adequately prepared us to understand the sociological, political, economic, medical, and spiritual depravity of the city. Being black, evangelical, and sincere did not make us equal to the challenges we faced.

Every day I saw clients who were less interested in my competence and compassion then they were interested in what I could accomplish with their forms. Can you write a letter? Can you get me on Social Security Disability? What about my medical assistance form? Few clients kept their appointments regularly and actually improved.

Our church neighbors were openly hostile. This is a bad place for a church. We don't need Jesus. We need jobs. With just ten or so regular attenders at our Sunday worship services, I fantasized about greener pastures far, far away.

In this valley of failure, I began to ask God's opinion on the matter. I literally stumbled across John Perkins' book *With Justice for All*. The Lord used this book to reframe my experiences and confront me with some haunting questions: If I don't provide compassionate care for the families who come to the public community mental health center, then who will? Can I count on my non-Christian psychiatric co-workers to advocate and genuinely care for their needs?

God's question to me was, "Did I send you to your own people in Philadelphia to be successful or to be faithful?" Three years after blundering and stumbling into inner-city ministry, my husband and I made a commitment to work for the Lord in the city of Philadelphia for at least twenty-five years, or until we developed new leadership.

In the years since, I have been faithful and God has been successful. At my community mental health center, I try to help my clients negotiate a complex system of psychiatric care. Since becoming medical director, I have been able to address problem areas that greatly irritated me in the past, such as the waiting list, crisis procedures, and appointment scheduling. My clients are all now doing extremely well due to my doctoring, or at least that's what they tell me.

In my neighborhood ministry alongside my husband, our consistent and caring presence has brought us acceptance. Four neighbors who criticized us for providing homes for substance abusers – because it was "making the community go downhill" – were knocking at our doors within a year or two, seeking help with addiction issues in their own families. Recently, I have been flooded with requests for psychiatric counseling from women who are familiar with our ministry – women who are poor, black, depressed, and frequently abused, women who would never go to a public mental health clinic. Mistrust of psychiatrists, counselors, and doctors is very high among our people, and I am deeply moved by their openness to me. I call it "success."

Today we constantly face the challenge of rejecting the world's view of success. This is hard, as we are required to keep track of the numbers for our many outreach activities. How many kids did you feed? How many clients did you see? How many bags of food did you give out? How many men and women do you have in your discipleship home? How many people accepted Christ? How many attend your church? It goes on and on.

If I had to do it all over again, would I still do it? Would I move into the inner city and live in the shadow of the housing projects? Would I choose to worship at a storefront church and spend the wee hours of the morning writing proposals to fund our youth ministry?

No, not if I had known the cost. Not if I had known how much heartbreak I would have to endure from seeing friends and neighbors changed by the power of God, only to return to the streets after a few months of sobriety. Not if I could have anticipated the thousands of hours and thousands of dollars out of my own pocket it would take for us to minister here. The price would have been far higher than I would have been prepared to pay.

But twelve years ago, not only was I able to count the cost; I was unable to imagine the rewards. I could not have imagined the joy of sharing my home once a week with seven teenage girls and imagining their transformation into young women of God. I could not have anticipated that Christ would transform a gun-toting drug dealer into a praise and worship leader. I would not have figured in the excitement in our kids' eyes as they boarded vans and buses for trips to the shore, Washington, D.C., and youth retreats. Least of all, I would not have been able to fathom the value of the peace that comes from being in the center of God's will.

Dr. Rosilyn Smith, M.D., is a psychiatrist with over thirty years of experience caring for adolescent, adult, and geriatric clients throughout the Greater Philadelphia Region. Dr. Smith received her medical degree from Wake Forest University School of Medicine and completed her training in psychiatry at Hahnemann University Hospital. As an addiction specialist, she treats clients with opiate, alcohol, cocaine, cannabis, nicotine, and PCP dependence. In addition to judiciously prescribing medications, Dr. Smith practices holistic medicine, encouraging wellness in the body, soul, and spirit. Rosilyn is a faith-sensitive psychiatrist, especially competent in cross cultural and interfaith care. She is optimistic that all her clients can enter full recovery. Her husband, Richard, has served as a home missionary pastor for many decades. Together they have developed specialized programs for substance abusers and children.

CHAPTER 26

GREAT EXPECTATIONS THAT DIDN'T PAN OUT

John Payne

The most important lessons I have learned during seventeen years of medical practice have come as surprises. I came to work with clear expectations, but in several major areas, reality clashed with my ideals.

Expectation #1: If you work with other Christians with whom you have gone to church, you will all have the same vision.
After completing my residency, I worked part-time for eight years as one of three physicians at Circle Family Care in Chicago, a clinic that operated as part of Circle Urban Ministries. During medical school, all physicians at the clinic had attended Circle Church – the church that gave birth to the clinic. I assumed that since we were all Christians and all coming out of a church committed to ministry among the poor, we would all be of one mind about how to carry out the ministry of the clinic.

In reality, staff members had serious disagreements about wheth-er the clinic should be operated primarily as a mission organization or as a professional organization. For example, we were divided over whether it was more important for counseling to be done by a

Christian or by a person of the same ethnicity as the clients.

One doctor wanted the clinic board to include professionals from the community who would give the clinic community credibility, even if their faith was not central to their lives. Another doctor wanted an all-Christian board. Which kind of board we had affected our fund-raising: to apply for federal grants, we had to have the community-based board, not the all-Christian board. Though we eventually arrived at a compromise, the process of getting there was so difficult that our solution never felt completely satisfactory to any of us.

While I was working at Circle Family Care, I was also teaching at Cook County Hospital. I found it far easier to work and teach in this secular setting because I didn't expect anyone there to share my values. One of my colleagues there was an Albanian Communist who was so hardline that she considered the Chinese Communists liberal. She and I got along great.

It was all a matter of expectations.

Expectation #2: There is no reason a group of white people cannot go into a black neighborhood and set up an effective ministry. Time revealed that it was a mistake for a primarily white church to plant a white ministry organization in a black neighborhood without first having strong spiritually-based black leadership in the ministry. It wasn't that African Americans were not involved in the ministry – some were. And it's not that we didn't want African Americans to share in leadership – we often wished for strong black leaders who could work with us. But the early leaders of the church and ministry were white, and were seen as a group of "do-gooders" who were not really a part of the community. Members of the community wondered if we were a weird cult rather than committed Christians, because the white church where many of the staff worshipped was unknown to them.

The situation was completely reversed when Raleigh Washington became pastor of Rock of Our Salvation Church, the primary church with which Circle Urban Ministries now partners. Raleigh's presence has filled the need for strong black leadership in the church and the ministry. The strength of the ministry now is a monument to God's power to use even our mistakes for God's glory.

Expectation #3: When I became director of a family residency program, I had an ideal opportunity to make clones of myself.
After eight years at Cook County Hospital and Circle, I moved to become director of a family medicine residency program in a small county hospital. The hospital felt like it had the same type of mission as Cook County, but it was smaller. "This is just the kind of setting," I thought, "that would be ideal for training someone to become just like me." And so I set out to train family residents to become just like me.

When I interviewed residency candidates, I didn't explicitly ask them religious questions, but I did ask questions about meaning and purpose, questions that often gave me insight into their faith and values.

I was also heavily involved in a Bible study for residents. Though not all the residents participated, many of the Christian residents did. Before long the residency program gained a reputation for being an excellent training program, but one that was open only to Christians. In reality, the program was open to non-Christians as well, but I had contributed to the appearance of discrimination by the nature of the questions I asked during interviews, and by the relationships I had with many of these residents not in the Bible study. Some of the residents not in the Bible study felt I favored those who were.

This eventually resulted in a grand jury investigation. In the end, the grand jury cleared me, acknowledging that I was screening for people who had servant hearts rather than selfish hearts, but I admit that this idea of making service the uniting principle was one on which I was not clear on when I came. It only became clear over time.

I backed off my original fantasy of trying to produce a few clones of myself, and instead concentrated on making one-percent changes in one hundred people by simply serving the people around me and modeling servanthood to the residents in my program. I found that it was far healthier to try to create an environment that encouraged residents to each become all God had created them to be, rather than to try to make them over in my image.

Expectation #4: I can do God's work on my own.
When I started practicing medicine, I wouldn't have actually said I could do God's work on my own, but all too often, my actions revealed that that's what I really believed. Feeling self-sufficient, I would work harder only to find that I was being less effective in my work and that I was not there for my family. This pattern eventually led me to confess to God, "I'm not such hot stuff that I can do this alone." I realized that I had to develop a consistent devotional life if I wanted to be as effective as I wanted to be, and as lead-able as I wanted to be, if I was to rely on God's power and not my own.

To help me in that, I found spiritual accountability in two places. First, I started meeting one-on-one with a physical therapist in my church whose spiritual life is very consistent. This person is not flashy, not an upfront leader, but he brings to the partnership a quiet, steady spirituality from which I can draw strength.

Second, my wife and I joined a weekly Bible study for couples. We joined because I got kicked out of the resident's Bible study when they decided that the residents needed me to leave, so they could use that setting to discuss freely the stresses they were experiencing in the program. Participating in this couples group, a group of people our age and in the same season of life, was an important source of peer support.

I can't do God's work alone. I must have God's power to do God's work. And to have God's power, I have learned that I need to draw on the regular support of peers to keep me spiritually accountable.

During these years, several of my most basic expectations about ministering through healthcare have bitten the dust when they collided with reality. God has replaced these mistaken assumptions with surprising new insights, often painfully won, that now guide my work. I'll be surprised if there aren't more surprises yet to come.

John Payne, MD, is currently the President of Medical Ambassadors International, an international network of people who are passionately committed to holistic missions. He has previously served with Circle Family Care, Cook County Hospital, and Stanislaus Family Medicine Residency. John is a graduate of Wheaton College, the University of Illinois Medical School, and the UC Davis Family Practice Residency in Stockton, CA. John and his wife, Madelle, have two children, both happily married, and four grandchildren.

CHAPTER

RELATIONSHIPS AND THE KINGDOM PERSPECTIVE

Irene Shomus Morrow

As I sat in the exam room with Jose, he told me why he woke up with nightmares and was unable to get back to sleep. He was a special-unit soldier for eight years in the Salvadoran army and worked closely with US advisors in fighting the war. He didn't need to say anymore; I had lived in rural El Salvador during the war and knew about the atrocities committed by the Salvadoran army. The American-trained special units had the worst reputation for brutality, and many of my co-worker's friends had been tortured and killed by the army.

In El Salvador, I would have feared him, but here in the confines of the community health center in eastern Washington, he is just a humble migrant worker with insomnia. His visit challenges the prejudices I hold toward certain categories of people. Because of his past involvements, I want to deny the serious post-traumatic stress disorder he suffers from, but God calls me to see Jose as an individual worthy of his love. I have to remind myself of the unconditional love of Jesus and the kingdom perspective he calls me to.

I have been a nurse practitioner in rural Mississippi, El Salvador, on the US/Mexico border, and now in eastern Washington. As I reflect on my past work, I can think of many issues that are important, even vital to long-term ministry: personal spiritual growth, nurturing family life, and supportive Christian community. Effective ministry is just not possible without attending to all of these issues.

I'm also convinced of two things: 1) The need to maintain Jesus' kingdom perspective, and 2) The need to allow ourselves to enter into relationships with those society often considers outcast.

After fifteen years in healthcare among the poor, it appears to get more difficult to do such work. One must be convinced of its importance to continue. Although it is essential to deal with issues like effective models, empowerment, and ownership, I also believe that if we only develop programs and do not allow ourselves to enter into friendship with those we serve, we miss out on how God can teach and transform us through relationships.

The Kingdom Perspective

The central theme of Jesus' life was the kingdom of God. He pointed to a kingdom where values were radically different than mainstream society. In this kingdom, good news was preached to the poor, the social misfits were accepted, and those with the most power and wealth were told to give it up to enter in. The most self-righteously religious were chastised for their lack of mercy and justice. The first were last, and the last were first. Those who attend to the needs of the "least of these" will enter into this kingdom.

Maintaining a kingdom perspective means being convinced of the importance of serving the poor. To ignore the poor and their needs is to ignore Jesus. Our spiritual life is intertwined with service and mercy.

Maintaining a kingdom perspective means being convinced of the importance of serving the poor. To ignore the poor and their needs is to ignore Jesus. Our spiritual life is intertwined with service and mercy. The "holistic gospel" calls us to see faith and action as inseparable. For me, the commitment to maintain a kingdom perspective is important because it is often not taught in churches. On the contrary, especially in today's anti-poor and anti-immigrant climate, the idea of serving the outcast is downright opposed. I sometimes get the feeling that evangelical Christians have replaced the hard sayings of Jesus to sell our possessions and give to the poor with the "Contract with America."[1] It appears that serving the poor will get more difficult and further challenge our faith and courage.

For example, Proposition 187 in California, which among other things denies healthcare to undocumented immigrants, also requires health personnel to report undocumented persons to Immigration and Naturalization Service. Will Christian health-care workers submit to such laws? What does Jesus call us to? I don't hear the church calling us to the radical life of Jesus that opposes the values of our materialistic culture. Without a commitment to the kingdom perspective of Jesus, it is difficult to face opposition and pursue advocacy and service among the poor.

I need to be convinced that working with the poor is part of the gospel. Otherwise, I might abandon such work for something easier. Healthcare for the poor is very difficult. Patients are usually sicker and have fewer options for care than those with wealth. To continue in such line of work we need to be convinced that ministry is more than just a job. Serving the poor is ministry and a call to faithfulness to God's word.

I remember working in a prenatal clinic in a remote area of El Salvador. I was taking histories while the midwife was doing exams. I had to ask how many pregnancies they had with how many births and how many living children. Each woman told me of her children who had died of malnutrition or pneumonia or diarrhea.

Finally, at the end of the day, I choked with tears as the last woman told me she had six pregnancies and births, and no living children. Her last two children, aged three and six, had died of measles two months earlier. Nothing in school or the church had prepared me to deal with the massive social injustice that allows children to die of malnutrition or simple diarrhea, or lack of basic health services.

The kingdom perspective that sustained me, by giving me hope in the face of despair, was that God was on the side of the poor and oppressed. Throughout Scripture God speaks in favor of the fatherless and the widow, the vulnerable, in society. In the book of Amos, the prophet Amos condemns injustice and exploiting the poor, and he calls the wealthy to compassion and upholding justice.

Relationships
One of the most important aspects of kingdom living is developing relationships with the poor. Relating involves acknowledging the fact that I have something to learn from others. God is relational, not distant or impersonal. He sent Jesus to be in a personal relationship. God's method of spreading the good news is through relationships. If God created all people in his image, how much we are missing when we limit our relationships to only those who are culturally, economically, and racially like us. We need relationships with the poor because we learn more of who God is – the God who chose to be born poor and homeless, who became a refugee in Egypt, and who was finally executed as a criminal. Through relationships, the poor become more than statistics and stereotypes. They become friends and individuals like myself with needs and hopes and dreams.

When working in South Texas our babysitter Lydia and her family became good friends with our family. Our kids played together, we shared meals often and went on outings to the beach. Lydia and Marcos are undocumented refugees from Central America. They were also patients at the clinic where I worked part time. When Lydia was diagnosed with appendicitis on my day off she told the doctor at the clinic she was going to call me to babysit her girls. The doctor was incredulous – women like Lydia were the maids for the providers, no provider would babysit for the maid. After this, the doctor referred to my co-dependent relationship with my patients. I had to think about this because I do think it is wrong to have unhealthy relationship with anyone, especially patients. But I think what bothered this doctor was that I was mingling with the wrong social class. And Jesus was also accused of this.[2]

In spite of the example of Jesus, friendship with the poor is not easy. Nor do I believe that we need to be bosom-buddies with all of our patients. It is clear from the example of Jesus that he was closer to some people than others. He was closer to Mary, Martha, Lazarus, and the disciples, for instance. But even those few we get close to can be challenging at times. For instance, since our children spent time at Lydia and Marcos' house, we were concerned about the unrestrained TV viewing in the home We finally had to tell them that we could not allow our kids to watch what they did on TV. We have remained friends and they have started screening TV shows. They asked us to be godparents to their daughter, and recently shared that they have become Christians and are attending church.

Lydia and Marcos continue to work in a restaurant, knowing that any day they may receive notice of deportation. They send money to their families in El Salvador and Nicaragua, and care for a nephew and niece whose parents recently divorced. Even though many with wealth and power despise Lydia and Marcos because of their refugee status, their friendship is a gift. We have learned about the love and grace of God through them.

Our relationship with Lydia and Marcos has helped us deal with our stereotypes of immigrants. When some folks in our church relayed their anti-immigrant sentiments to us, we shared about Lydia and Marcos, our godchild, and our son's playmates. We spoke of the nightmare of their journey here and their hopes for peace now. That group of "illegal immigrants" is not a faceless crowd to us. Instead, we have friends and brothers and sisters in Christ in that crowd.

That is why the kingdom perspective demands that we make relationships with the so-called outcasts; our lives become intertwined, and we see their suffering and fear up-close. Then they are not evil enemies, but fellow humans, who need God's love and mercy.

So, I return to Jose in the exam room. My urge is to see him as a part of an evil group. However, Jesus' perspective calls me to view him – not as a Salvadoran soldier, not as an illegal alien, not as a migrant worker – but as one whom God loves and for whom Jesus gave his life and to whom he offers forgiveness. For this reason, God

calls me to preserve in ministry with the poor: developing relationships, maintaining his kingdom perspective, and allowing myself to
be transformed by those from whom I least expect it.

But God chose the foolish things of the world to shame the wise;
God chose the weak things of the world to shame the strong. He
chose the lowly things of this world and the despised things – and the
things that are no – to nullify the things that are that no one may
boast before him.[3]

*Irene Schomus Morrow is a Registered Nurse Practitioner and
Diabetes Educator working with the CVCH Diabetes and Nutrition
Program. She has worked in many different areas with diverse popu-
lations. She practiced community health nursing in rural Mississippi,
trained health promoters in rural El Salvador, and worked with
Central American refugees in South Texas. She has worked to
develop diabetes programs at Moses Lake Community Health,
Samaritan Healthcare, and Central Washington Hospital.*

CHAPTER 28

LEARNING TO LET OTHERS SERVE ME

J.D. Miller

In 1973, straight out of my residency in Cleveland, I moved to Evarts, Kentucky, a small Appalachian coal town in Harlan County, in the extreme southeast corner of the state. There I joined the staff of Clover Fork Clinic, a community-based clinic being launched with the help of a five-year start-up grant from the federal government.

Looking back over twenty-two years at the clinic, I can see three major lessons I have learned.

1. Don't try to go it alone.

I am a Mennonite, and when I came here there were a few other Mennonite families in the area, most of them, but not all, working in healthcare. The fact that I knew other Mennonites in the area was a factor in my coming. One of them, in fact, was key to recruiting me.

But when I came, I had little idea how critical the presence of a community of like-minded people would be to my ability to make it in my work. A few months after I arrived, several Mennonite families who were attending various area churches began a home fellowship group. Eventually that group got into a study of John Driver's book,

Community and Commitment, which outlines a vision of the church. Through that study we realized that if we were going to have a church anything like what we were talking about, we needed to start our own church. So, in 1977, about four years after I had moved to the area, we started Harlan Mennonite Fellowship.

These people have been my support network. This community of people who share my values has, more than anything else, made it possible for me to stay here this long.

I once precepted a Jewish medical student who was so impressed with the role my Mennonite community played in supporting me in the work that he told me, "I need to look for the same kind of support network – a Jewish community – in choosing where I'm going to practice."

2. Don't be too quick with solutions.

I am amazed at how many volunteers come here for a week or so to work on a project and go home thinking they know the answers to Appalachia's problem. I've learned that when someone goes into an underserved area "to save the people," people resent it. Far better is it to come with the goal of becoming part of the people.

When I first came here, I lived in a housing development quite a ways away from the clinic. After about four years, I moved closer to my clinic. I think that moved made me much more a part of the community in people's eyes.

I've had to learn the community's culture. I grew up on an Iowa farm. The culture here is similar. In some ways the pace of life is slower here. For example, when I call my banker, if I start telling him my business right away, he stops me and asks how I'm doing and visits a bit, then goes on with our business.

In the same way, I've learned to slow down when seeing patients. I start out by visiting more than I used to, and during patient visits we talk a lot more. What we talk about sometimes helps me understand their health issues. People here deal with a lot of anxiety and depression growing out of their sense of powerlessness. The stories patients tell me often give me insight into why they're anxious.

Instead of coming into the community with answers, I've learned that it is far more important to come with the goal of working hard at getting to know the people. I have become enough a part of the community that I feel their feelings and see things through their eyes. When they get tears in their eyes, I get tears in mine. I feel their frustrations with them. And this identification gives me insight into many things that otherwise wouldn't make sense.

3. Precept students for your own sake.

I have precepted a few students through the CCHF preceptorship program, more through a Mennonite program, and some through secular organizations. I started doing it mostly to help the students, but along the way I discovered that I needed to precept because of what I get out of it. Precepting keeps me up to date medically; students keep me aware of the latest developments in medicine. It also challenges me spiritually, because students ask tough questions and force me to wrestle with them.

I came to Harlan County twenty-two years ago because I wanted to serve in an underserved area. The lessons I have learned, though, have been mostly about letting others serve me – my faith community, my patients, the people of the community, and the students I precept. I might have come here thinking I had solutions to offer. What I've found is something far better than the opportunity to dispense solutions. I've found a sense of belonging – a community where people care about me, where I care about them, where we look out for each other.

J.D. Miller, MD, has worked as a primary care physician in rural Appalachia since 1973. Currently, he is Vice President of Medical Affairs for Appalachian Regional Healthcare.

NOTES

INTRODUCTION

1 Isaiah 58:6-12
2 Matthew 6:10
3 Matthew 6:6-13, 33
4 Luke 4:18-19
5 Matthew 10:1-8; Luke 10:9
6 Acts 10:34-38
7 John 14:12-14
8 Acts 8:6-8
9 Acts 14:3; 8-10; Acts 9:10-19
10 Matthew 25:31-46
11 1 Corinthians 12:28
12 James 5:14-15
13 St. Basil the Great: A Study in Monasticism; W.K. Lowther Clarke; Cambridge University Press, New York; pages 61-62

CHAPTER 2 - WITNESS TO INJUSTICE

1 Micah 6:8
2 Garfield, Rachel, Melissa Majerol, et. al. Kaiser Family Foundation, "The Uninsured: A Primer, Key Facts About Americans Without Health Coverage" Dec 2014. http://kff.org/uninsured/report/the-uninsured-a-primer/view
3 New England Journal of Medicine, 2011; 364:2343-33

CHAPTER 3 - THE PUBLIC HELL UNDER THE EL

1 McNeill, John. Taking a Chance on God: Liberating Theology for Gays, Lesbians, and Their Lovers, Families, and Friends. 1996. Beacon Press: Boston, MA.

CHAPTER 5 - BIBLICAL FOUNDATIONS FOR EMPOWERING THE POOR

1 Exodus 3:7-8
2 Luke 4:18-19; Isaiah 61:1-2
3 Luke 1:52-53
4 James 5:1
5 Jeremiah 5:26-28
6 Isaiah 3:14-15

7   Amos 5:21-22
8   Amos 5:12
9   Matthew 25:31-46
10   1 John 3:17
11   www.phillyhistory.org/blog/index.php/2011/08/why-remember-edison-high-school/
12   Amos 2:6
13   Amos 2:7
14   Psalm 94:20
15   Isaiah 10:1-2
16   Amos 4:1-2
17   Leviticus 25:8-28
18   Deuteronomy 15:1-11
19   Acts 4:34-35
20   2 Corinthians 8:13-14
21   Exodus 20:15,17; Deuteronomy 5:19, 21
22   Psalm 24:1
23   Leviticus 25:23
24   www.biography.com/people/mahatma-ghandi
25   Bernard Wideman, "Dominating the Pineapple Trade," *Far Eastern Economic Review*, 8 July 1974
26   Trends in Malaria Morbidity and Mortality in Sri Lanka. www.NCBI.nlm.nih.gov/pubmed/8405594
27   John 12:24-26

CHAPTER 6 – MEDICINE AS MINISTRY WITH THE POOR

1   Deuteronomy 15:7-11
2   Ezekiel 34:2-4
3   Luke 10:25-37
4   II Corinthians 1:4
5   https://en.wikipedia.org/wiki/Basil_of_Caesarea#Writings

CHAPTER 7 – THE STATUS AND WORTH OF WOMEN: A BIBLICAL PERSPECTIVE

1   Exodus 18:4
2   Psalm 27:9
3   Calvin, John. *The Second Epistle of Paul the Apostle to the Corinthians*. p. 217
4   Luke 13:16

5   John 11:25
6   Mark 16:14
7   Luke 11:27-28
8   Leviticus 15:25
9   Mark 5:34
10   John 8:1-11
11   Matthew 23:37
12   Luke 15:8-10
13   Matthew 11:28

CHAPTER 8 - HOW DO YOU KEEP GOING?
1   2 Corinthians 1:8-9

CHAPTER 9 - LOVE IS THE MARK
1   Hemfelt, Robert and Richard Fowler. *Serenity: A Companion for Twelve Step Recovery*. 2010. Thomas Nelson.

CHAPTER 11 - THROWING DOWN THE ROD
1   Exodus 3-4
2   Proverbs 11:24-25

CHAPTER 12 - TO PLEASE GOD
1   Luke 4:18
2   Matthew 25:31-46
3   Colossians 3:23-24
4   Luke 8:44-48
5   Matthew 15:22-28
6   Luke 8:10-17
7   Luke 9:58
8   Luke 10:7
9   Luke 12:51
10   Luke 18:22
11   Mark 1:35-38
12   John 5:1-14
13   Philippians 3:17; I Timothy 4:12
14   Matthew 7:4
15   I Peter 1:16

CHAPTER 13 – MYTHS ABOUT MEDICAL SCHOOL

1   Chekhov, A. *A Boring Story*, 1889. Chekhov was a physician and is known as the greatest short story writer in history.

2   Wingard, J.R., and Williamson, J.W., "Grades as Predictors of Physician's Career Performance: An Evaluative Literature Review," J. Med. Educ., Vol. 48, 1973. pp. 311-322

3   Turner, EX. Helper, M.M., and Kriska, S.D., "Predictors of Clinical Performance," J. Med. Educ., Vol. 49, 1974, pp. 338-342

4   Gough, H.G., "Some Predictive Implications of Premedical Scientific Competence and Preferences," J. Med. Educ., Vol. 53, 1978, 00. 291-300

5   Browne, S., "The Christian Role in Medicine," in Medicine and the Christian Mind, Allister Vale, ed., London: Christian Medical Fellowship Publications, 1980.

6   Galatians 1:10; 2 Corinthians 10:12

7   Payne, F., Biblical/Medical Ethics, Milford, Michigan: Mott Media, 1985, p. 57.

8   Pelligrino, J.P., "Educating the Christian Physician," in Whole-Person Medicine, David E. Allen, Lewis P. Bird and Robert Herrmann, eds., Downers Grove, Illinois: Intervarsity Press, 1980, pp. 103-104.

9   Burkitt, D.P., Our Priorities, London: Christian Medical Fellowship Publication, 1976, p. 12.

10 Hilton, D., "A Challenge to Complete the US Healthcare System," H 6t D (Health and Development), Fall, 1988, p. 12.

11 West, L.J., et al., "Alcoholism," Ann. Intern. Med., Vol 100, 1984, pp. 405-416.

12 Zelnik, M., "Sexual Activity Among Adolescents: Perspective of a Decade," in McAnarney, E.R. Premature Adolescent Pregnancy and Parenthood, New York: Grune & Stratton, 1983, pp. 21-33.

13 Barnes, D.M., "Drugs: Running the Numbers," Science, Vol. 240, June 1988, pp. 1729-1731.

14 Myers, J.K., et al., "Six Month Prevalence of Psychiatric Disorders in Three Communities," Arch. Gen. Psychiatry, Vol. 41, 1984, pp. 959967.

15 Najjar, M.F., Rowland, M., "Anthropometric Reference Date and Prevalence of Overweight – United States, 1976-90," Hyattsville, MD: U.S. Department of Health and Human Services, Public Health Service, 1987, DHHS publication no. (PHS) 87-1688, Vital Health and Statistics, series 11, no. 238.

16 Parker, R.L., ed., The Journal of John Wesley, Chicago: Moody, 1974, p. 231, as quoted in Payne F., Biblical/Medical Ethics.

17 Matthew 16:26, paraphrased

CHAPTER 14 - CALLED TO SERVE? DON'T LET HEALTHCARE EDUCATION DEBT STAND IN YOUR WAY

1   David, Jonathan. "Medical Education Needs Major Surgery." WSJ. N.p., 26 Sept. 2013. Web. 06 August 2015.

2   Denhart, Chris. "How The $1.2 Trillion College Debt Crisis Is Crippling Students, Parents And The Economy." Forbes. *Forbes Magazine*, 7 Aug. 2013. Web.

CHAPTER 15 - DON'T MISS THE BANQUET

1   Matthew 11:28-30

2   Luke 14:11

3   Luke 14:13

4   Revelation 19:9

5   Luke 14:16-24

6   Genesis 3:17-19

7   Augustine, Saint Bishop of Hippo; Carolyn J.B. Hammond. Cambridge: Mass: Harvard University Press, 2014-

8   I Corinthians 9:9

9   Matthew 25:14-30

10   Matthew 22:30

11   Ecclesiastes 4:12

CHAPTER 17 - THE THIRTY-SIX-HOUR DAY

1   "The Thirty Six Hour Day" CBS. *60 Minutes*. Marion Goldin, Mike Wallace. CBS News. New York, NY. 1987. VHS video. Worldcat database.

2   Proverbs 16:9; Romans 8:28

3   Matthew 16:26

4   II Corinthians 12:9-10

5   http://www.nejm.org/doi/full/10.1056/NEJMp1202848

6   http://www.nytimes.com/2014/09/05/opinion/why-do-doctors-commit-suicide.html

CHAPTER 19 - MISSIONAL COMPONENTS OF A CHRISTIAN HEALTH MINISTRY

1   Proverbs 19:21

2   Genesis 1:27-30

3   Matthew 28:18

4   Acts 13:36

5   Matthew 10:1,7-8
6   Matthew 16:19
7   Luke 4:16-19
8   Numbers 11:4-29
9   Acts 2:14-18
10   Matthew 5:10-12

CHAPTER 20 - THE CHOICES: HOW CAN I BEST SERVE?

1   Luke 12:42-43
2   Matthew 25:14-28
3   Luke 12:32-34
4   Galatians 5:13

CHAPTER 21 - WHERE DOES HEALTH COME FROM? A CHALLENGE TO COMPLETE THE US HEALTHCARE SYSTEM

1   Judges 17:6; 21:25
2   James 5:14-15
3   II Chronicles 7:14

CHAPTER 22 - LEARNING TO PRAY FOR HEALING

1   Psalm 78:41
2   Matthew 8:16-17; Psalm 103:5
3   Luke 4:39, 41
4   John 20:19-22
5   Mark 16:15-18
6   Acts 3:6, 6:8, 8:4-8, 9:17-18, 28:7-10
7   Healing: The Three Great Classics on Divine Healing, Compiled and
     Edited by Jonathan L. Graf. Camp Hill, PA: Christian Publications,
     1992. Pp. 155-159, 271-275.
8   I Corinthians 12
9   Matthew 7:7, 9:38; John 16:23-24; James 1:5, 4:2; 1 John 5:14;
     Luke 11:9
10   I Corinthians 12:9, 28, 30
11   Matthew 26:39
12   Matthew 6:9-14
13   Galatians 4:13-14; Philippians 2:26-27; II Corinthians 12:7;
     I Timothy 5:23; II Timothy 4:20; Hebrews 2:10, 5:7-9 NLT
14   I Timothy 2:4
15   Romans 4:17-25

16   Exodus 15:26
17   II Chronicles 16:12
18   Colossians 1:20
19   John 2:6 NLT

CHAPTER 27 - RELATIONSHIPS AND THE KINGDOM PERSPECTIVE
1   www.u-s-history.com/pages/h2052.html
2   Luke 15:2
3   I Corinthians 1:27-29

ADDENDUM

Our Mission

The mission of CCHF is to engage, encourage and equip Christians to live out the gospel through healthcare among the poor.

Our Values

Supremacy of Christ: Honoring the Lordship of Christ and submitting ourselves to his authority and person.

Prophetic Voice: Challenging God's people to choose to go against the status quo: to be incarnational, sacrificial, and to enter into the suffering of the poor.

Wholistic Care: Encouraging excellent, compassionate health care, ministering to spiritual, physical, and emotional needs of people and their communities.

Reconciliation: Restoring right relationships to God, to one another, and to all of creation, addressing barriers that commonly divide, including race, social status, and economic oppression.

Justice: Working toward God's kingdom, setting all things right for the oppressed, the forgotten, and particularly the marginalized in our health care system.

Partnership: Listening to and working alongside churches, patients, our communities, and one another.

Our Role

We believe that there is a growing movement of Christians who are committed to bring healing to marginalized communities in Jesus' name. CCHF is the joint effort of those in the movement to help others find their place in our common cause, persevere in our mutual calling, and grow in our understanding of what it means to be ambassadors of Christ in healthcare and in communities of need.

Simply put, the role of CCHF is to support and grow this movement. We do this by:

Relational Network

The most powerful thing about CCHF is the actual community. It is real. It is relational. It is a family. We are committed to each other's success. So, like the body of Christ, we share our experiences and insights with one another and help one another any way we can. I love the part of my job that helps members of the CCHF family find one another and connect in meaningful ways that honors Christ and advances His cause.

National and Regional Events

The biggest and most visible of these is the annual CCHF conference. It is a 3-day event with inspiring speakers, informative workshops, and potent times of networking. Major Christian leaders and pioneers make themselves available to sit with newcomers, to both share and to listen to the new voices that God is raising up in this community.

Students and Residents

A big part of what we do is reaching out to Christians during their training years. Through collaborative relationships with groups like CMDA, MCO and Intervarsity, we send practitioners to speak to campus groups at medical, dental, nursing, PA and behavioral health campuses. We provide clinical experiences through a network of preceptor and internship programs in Christian clinics. And when the time comes, we help residents find placements at clinics where they can integrate faith with clinical care for the medically underserved.

Publications
Health & Development, (H&D) is a journal that is published by CCHF. It is a non-commercial periodical where Christian professionals working with the medically underserved share their stories and explore the unique challenges encountered in providing holistic, Christ-driven care in domestic cross-cultural settings.

www.CCHF.org
This website is designed to be a tool shed where members of the movement share resources to help you grow in your conviction and ability to fulfill a calling in healthcare as an integrated part of your walk with Christ. It is constantly changing and growing. Our community adds content, and the dialogue continues as we wrestle with what it means to live out the gospel through healthcare among the poor.

To connect with CCHF, send us a note at info@cchfmail.org.